STORIES OF SCOTLAND

LANG SYNE PUBLISHERS LTD.

INTRODUCTION

"Stories of Scotland" is three books in one.

The first is a collection of 10 stories penned by popular Scottish writers; the second, Scottish Stories of the Supernatural, consists of eerie tales of ghosts and strange happenings; the third, Scottish Shipwreck and Disaster Stories, features gripping accounts of some of the worst tragedies to befall our shores — from terrible loss of life at sea to death in the dark below ground.

The first, and longest story, is a fictional piece set in Edinburgh more than 30 years ago at Festival time. It is full of high drama and the action is located in some of the city's best known streets and landmarks.

The second, from Rennie McOwan, offers a unique angle on events surrounding the ill-fated Battle of Culloden which killed off Bonnie Prince Charlie's dreams of becoming king of Scotland and England.

Both these stories are published for the first time.

The rest of the stories in Book One are based on actual events and were previously published in diffferent editions of the Scots Magazine.

★ Glasgow ship owner John McDougall sank his own ships to claim the insurance — but an old beggar woman selling cloth in the streets was to prove the unlikely cause of his downfall.

★ A Scots teenage girl captured by pirates on the high seas seemed destined to spend the rest of her life trapped in slavery — but she ended up Empress of Morocco.

★ Non-stop rainstorms in Morayshire caused rivers to rise 50 feet above their banks and Elgin was totally surrounded by water looking like a city built on an island. Locals believed the Lord had delivered a localised version of the Great Flood as a punishment for their sins.

★ The first major conflict on Scottish soil was fought over 1900 years ago — but where is the actual site?

★ From the Borders there are tales of the wee folk who stole babies and made those who befriended them prosper. From the Highlands come accounts of dark deeds and eerie happenings in Niall Brownlie's chapter on the Badenoch Witches.

★ From old Glasgow an insight into the standards in the community. Adulterers were ducked in the Clyde, special permission was needed from the minister before a midwife could visit a single pregnant woman, and those found guilty of assault were drummed out of town. If they came back they'd be hanged.

★ Eleven women accused of witchcraft were once locked up in Lanark to await trial and from this event Dorothy K Haynes spins a fine wee short story ....

All the material in Scottish Stories of the Supernatural is written by James K Monaghan who says: 'From clachans, castles, shielings, and even bothies come tales of the second sight, phantasms of the living, apparitions of the dead, the peculiar occurrencies prior to a death, fairies, witches, mermaids and the strange unknown creatures from loch, mountain and river.

In these pages I tell of the family who knew they were doomed because of physical deformities which afflicted four of their neighbours .... one was buck-toothed, one hare-lipped, another half-witted and the fourth a stammerer.

I tell of the caravanner who was launched to his death over a cliff by the ghosts of clansmen long dead. Hours earlier he had disturbed their mass grave while exploring.

You can find out, too, about kelpies. These mysterious creatures of the deep had a dual use for the hundreds of unsuspecting travellers whom they trapped. The horse-like beasts devoured the flesh themselves whilst the person's soul was handed to the Devil.

Other stories reveal what happens when the Devil's disciples gather on certain nights of the year, what caused two men to be reduced to dust in an instant when they entered church, why the ghost of a dog beaten to death after being wrongly branded a baby killer still wails in the hills, how a labourer was held prisoner for seven years after digging up a piece of turf that was the roof of a fairy woman's house, and the special protection offered by a cross of rowan twigs or cold iron in the form of a horseshoe placed above the door.

Then there is the astonishing story of three Scots soldiers who shot at a wayside shrine of the Madonna — one knocked off a foot, another only chipped the raised finger. But the third soldier shattered it eventually. What subsequently happened to them in real life mirrored the damage each had inflicted on the figure.

How did a brother prove to his sister that he was a ghost? Ingredients for this yarn include an agonising wound inflicted by the brother, phantom writings in a diary, and a grim prophecy.

I reveal the curious experiences of my brother who gave shelter and food to a young mother and her baby at his Highland railway station. But were they from beyond the grave? And what makes such a conclusion seem more probable than improbable?

In other pages there is the curious case of the bell that wouldn't stop ringing, the phantoms of tenth century Vikings who still attack a Scottish island to this day, invisible ghosts, and weird creatures named glaistigs, urisks and trows.

As John Buchan once wrote of the north of Scotland: "It is the land on the edge of moorlands and the ruins of forests and the twilight before the dawn and strange knowledge dwells in it".

The range of topics is very extensive and in making a selection for you, my hope is merely to interest and entertain with perhaps just the possibility of lifting a tiny corner of the heavy veil that separates us from the vast unknown.'

The first story in "Scottish Shipwreck and Disaster Stories" features the Eyemouth disaster. Without warning a howling hurricane blew up in the sea and 189 fishermen were lost. The events of that day are recalled by J M Russell in "Victims of the Black Storm."

Fourteen years later, in 1895, the demise on rocks near the Isle of Coll of the 4500-ton Nessmore was a shipwreck drama of a very different kind. Simon Martin was one of a group of young divers who re-discovered the wreck a few years ago. He tells the Whisky Galore! style story behind the washing ashore of much of the cargo including valuable cattle, cheese, flour, apples and even musical instruments.

On another occasion the cruel sea claimed 45 lives when the "Forfarshire", then the largest sea-going steamer to be built in Dundee, went down. But the disaster could have been worse had it not been for the courage and daring shown by a young lady called Grace Darling who snatched a group of passengers from the jaws of death in a daring rescue. A H Millar tells the full story.

A stirring eye-witness account of the events surrounding Britain's worst rail disaster is given by Edwin S Towill. As a small boy he saw the dead and injured being ferried from the scene of carnage in Dumfriesshire after a triple crash which claimed 227 lives.

The disaster in Dumfries highlighted by Jonh R Smith took an entire autumn to engulf its 420 victims. It came in the form of the dreaded cholera which had spread from Asia with the first British case being recorded in Sunderland the year before.

Other stories tell of:-

★ The 70 children who died in a Paisley cinema trying to escape a threat that did not exist.

★ The 209 Blantyre miners torn apart in an explosion which had been feared for days because of a big gas build-up underground.

★ The Fife miners and their rescuers engulfed in thousands of tons of moss.

★ The sinking of a car ferry on its way from Stranraer to Larne with the loss of 133 lives.

★ The train that plunged from the Tay Bridge during a violent storm.

★ The collapse of a Glasgow bank and how it spelt disaster of a financial nature for many — and terms of imprisonment for the directors.

★ The 66 soccer fans suffocated to death on Stairway 13 at Ibrox in 1971. The victims included five teenage lads from the same street; a man who had doubts about going to the match because of his boy's birthday and then changed his mind; and an emigrant father and son on their first visit home to Scotland after seven years in Canada.

The final story is different from the rest in that we can't say for sure whether the events portrayed really did happen. Many believe they did. It centres on Aberdeen sailor Allan Gordon whose ship foundered on the Arctic ice. He survived and struck up a remarkable friendship with a polar bear — a friendship that was later to save his life when all the occupants of the village in which he settled were eaten alive by a pack of bears.

"STORIES OF SCOTLAND"
PUBLISHER'S NOTE

"STORIES OF SCOTLAND", INCORPORATING "Scottish Stories of the Supernatural" and "Scottish Shipwreck and Disaster Stories".
First published by Lang Syne Publishers Ltd., 45 Finnieston Street, Glasgow G3 8JU.
Printed by Dave Barr Print, 45 Finnieston Street, Glasgow G3 8JU.

© LANG SYNE PUBLISHERS LTD. 1986.

First published 1986. Reprinted 1994.

ISBN 0 946264 88 0

Cover illustration: A view of the Battle of Culloden courtesy of E.T. Archive. See the story, by Rennie McOwan, entitled "A Clansman at Culloden".

Contributors to the general story section: John Mckay, Rennie McOwan, John Bonnar, A.C. McKerracher, Dorothy K. Haynes, Alex R. Mitchell, Niall M. Brownlie, David Fergus, Patricia Hughes and Gordon Maxwell. Illustrated by John Mckay.

"Scottish Stories of the Supernatural" is written by James K. Monaghan and illustrated by David Whitton. Originally published by Lang Syne as a single volume in 1983. Lead illustration: Hounds of Hell pursue the evil laird (see story 8).

Contributors to "Scottish Shipwreck and Disaster Stories" are: Ian Andsell, J.M. Russell, Edwin S. Towill, Simon Martin, A.H. Millar, George Skinner, John R. Smith, Archibald A. Lawrie, Kent Mair and Sheila Allan. Illustrated by David Whitton. Originally published by Lang Syne as a single volume in 1983. Lead illustration: Clinging to Life in the Stormy Seas. The stories by J.M. Russell, Simon Martin, George Skinner, John R. Smith, Archibald A. Lawrie and Sheila Allan were originally published in The Scots Magazine.

Our thanks to Mr Maurice Fleming, Editor of The Scots Magazine, and contributors for giving us permission to reprint stories from the magazine.

Criminal Camera!
An Edinburgh plot

By JOHN MACKAY

When young Robert Hart spoke to the girl outside the Usher Hall on the opening night of the Festival, he was not to know that both of them would become involved with criminals.

He had been told there was often an attempt by last-minute visitors to Edinburgh to try at the Hall itself for tickets for the Sunday opening concert. Having been given two tickets for free the day before, and although the concert was not just his musical taste, he had the romantic idea since he was fancy-free at the moment of going to the Hall entrance an hour or so before the concert began to wait until he saw some pretty young lady come out of one of the Hall doorways with a disappointed look on her face. He would then ask her if she would care for one of his tickets.

When this actually happened and the girl was about to pass, he managed to blurt out: "Excuse me miss, were you looking for a ticket for this concert?"

June Ralston of London, newly arrived for the Festival and staying with her maiden aunt, was well accustomed to the male approach. She looked at the blunt-nosed, square-set, healthy-looking specimen before her and said: "Yes, have you one for sale?"

"For sale? No," he protested, "I mean would you share a seat with me — I mean two seats — it's just that I've got these two tickets and ..."

"You mean you're sort of offering me the seat as a gift?" she asked.

"Yes, that's it".

"Thank you very much — the white heather I bought this morning has brought me luck", smiled the girl.

Robert, suppressing a desire to do cartwheels along the pavement, led the way to the main doorway.

"Our seats are in the Grand Circle" he announced as they went up the stairway of ivory and gold.

He decided that Fate must be with him arranging for this to happen on a week's holiday long overdue from the advertising agency where he worked.

She was thinking that her latest boyfriend in London was in comparison an overdressed bore and glad now for the impulse that had brought her to Scotland.

She also decided she would like to get to know this young man better and maybe introduce him to her aunt tomorow, if he was free.

* * * * * * * * *

Indeed he had been free, and they had met again at the Usher Hall door in the early afternoon of Monday and were now climbing the stairs again — this time, up the Nelson Column on Calton Hill — the best view as an introduction to the City and its surroundings Robert had said.

When they were nearing the top, a sound like muted thunder rumbled down the interior of the column.

June, wide-eyed, stopped and looked a question at her companion.

"That was the sound of the one o'clock time ball coming down the shaft of the mast on top of the monument", explained Robert.

"Sorry, I should have mentioned it before. An apprentice from the firm who look after the City clocks comes up every week-day to wind up the mechanism".

They met the apprentice as they reached the top of the public stairway. He was just coming out of the door marked NO ADMISSION which led to the upper balcony, and the lad, much flattered by June's interest, told them all about his job.

After his footsteps had clattered off downstairs, June and Robert walked round the balcony. He pointed out features of the skyline of the Old Town silhouetted against the heat-haze. Then he noticed that the apprentice had forgotten to lock the NO ADMISSION door. The door, handleless, swung open at a touch, disclosing another stair beside a cog-wheeled metal column, leading to the top-most balcony where the time ball rested at the base of the mast.

"Let's go up", suggested Robert.

"Not allowed".

"Och, come on. There's nobody to stop us, and you can always say you've been where no other visitors had got to".

"Just for a minute then", said June, loking fastidiously into the dusty, oily half-gloom of the circular room before following Robert up the short stairway.

There was just room for them on that topmost small balcony — them, and the time ball huge in close up.

"What about taking it home for a souvenir", grinned Robert — then his expression changed and he whispered, "Someone coming up the main stair, we'd better get down ... easy now ... let me help you".

A now worried girl and a keenly listening young man stood at the inside of the NO ADMISSION door. "Too late to chance going out ... they've arrived, whoever they are ... we'll stay behind this door, maybe they'll just go round and down again", he whispered into her ear.

But 'they' stayed quite a while, with the two behind the door suppressing fits of laughter while straining to catch the very odd conversation going on beyond their hiding place.

"Why", whined a youngish Cockney voice, "did we have to come up here in all this flamin' bloody heat anyway?"

"Because, Syd", answered a breathless, more mature and slightly cultured voice, "I'm a top class photographer who sees this as a vantage point for subject matter for my files — always assuming I'll be a free man after Thursday night, that is".

If the two listening could have seen him they'd have wondered at the momentary expression of fear that showed on his florid face. Then he continued:"But why shouldn't we be free after Thursday, eh? If there's a hitch we play it straight; if things go to plan, the earliest they may find out is on Friday — in fact they maybe'll never find out for a long time. All we've got to do is keep calm and think of the money".

In the silence that followed, the click of a camera could be heard once or twice then the photographer again: "Now remember Syd, get that phrase into your head. Remember to ..."

The rest of the sentence was lost as the strange pair moved round to the west side of the balcony. June raised her eyebrows and nodded at the door beside them. Robert shook his head.

"Wait", he whispered, "I'd hate them to find out that they've not been alone. We'll be all right here".

At last the photographer and his apparent assistant came round again to the head of the public stairway and before descending June and Robert heard the photographer saying "And whatever happens remember the cue — remember when I say NOTE THE REFLECTOR GENTLEMEN, you make the move on the word GENTLEMEN ... remember now, remember the cue ..."

* * * * * * * * *

"O.K.", breathed Robert, and he stepped out onto the public balcony. Cautiously looking down he said, "Keep low, June, in case they spot us when they get to the roundabout — I think that'll be their car, the red Triumph Herald — yes, number 1208 SF — we'll note that for future reference because there'e something funny going to happen in Edinburgh in the next few days, or my name ain't Robert Hart — and I don't mean funny ha-ha either".

Before going down, June and Robert watched from the balcony and saw the red Herald leave Calton Hill and reappear in Waterloo Place where it turned right.

"Wait now", said Robert, "see if it comes down Leith Walk way".

They turned to the north-facing side of the balcony.

No red car. "That means they've either gone up East Register Street or down Broughton Street or into Gayfield Square; maybe staying around where your aunt lives".

"Always supposing they're staying in Edinburgh" added June. And on that unhelpful note they wandered down the hill in the summer heat to the east end of the New Town and to one of the small quiet streets where June's aunt Miss Macower lived.

* * * * * * * * *

Looking for a particular car in Edinburgh especially at Festival time is like looking for a needle in a haystack thought Robert on his way home that Monday evening. He knew the car's number, its colour and that the driver was probably staying in town. He must, he decided, try some of the garages in the morning. Further thought on the day's happenings included the business of something going to occur on Thursday; and why that phrase "Note the reflector?"

As he arrived at his lone 'digs' in the Marchmont area he had decided he would continue to play detective. He was NOT going to do the sensible thing and inform the Police about what they had overheard; first, because he was determined June must not be involved, and second, for fear of making a fool of himself. They'd be bound to ask what he was doing up in the NO ADMISSION part of the balcony. But the main reason for keeping it quiet was to show off to (what he hoped) was to be HIS girl. With next morning's meeting to look forward to, Robert Hart eventually got to bed, and, trying the word 'June' over in various cadences, eventually got to sleep.

* * * * * * * * *

Robert, much too early for his meeting with June, found she was even earlier. Her eyes were bright with excitement: "I've found them, Robert, I've found the car — the man's name is Prendiss — he's living near us I think — they're going to the Canongate this morning — at half past eleven to Charlie's — I was up early, couldn't sleep — had a walk before breakfast — struck lucky at the third garage".

Before Robert could speak she was off again: "A young lad just opening the gates, I asked had they a red Herald and gave the number — he said they had — I hinted the driver was a suspicious character and could he keep my enquiry secret and he said anything you say, miss — I asked if he knew where they were staying — he didn't but had an idea it wasn't far away and added that they were collecting the car at a quarter past eleven to pick up the case from Charlie's in the Canongate and —"

"How did he know that last bit?" cut in Robert.

"Because he was working behind another car and overheard — smart lad — I wanted to ask more but a mechanic appeared so I said remember it's a secret and the lad gave me a wink".

Robert, feeling his detective act was being taken over, and not much liking the wink business, had however the grace to say: "Well done, June, you'd get a job with the CID no bother; but we have time to do our walk down the Royal Mile as planned and still be in the Canongate well before eleven".

"To find Charlie's?" asked June.

Robert nodded.

*   *   *   *   *   ⌐   *   *   *   *

"Charlie? Charlie? Oh aye, even the bairns ca' him that, although they're feared for him, ever since he set up a wee burglar alarm, hame made and it nearly blew the breeks off one o' them climbin' up the windae at the back o' the shop". Their informant, a dealer in what appeared to be mostly brassware, continued: "Oh aye, could be an instrument maker — great for gadgets though I never could get seein' what goes on in that wee workshop o' his — foreigner of course — and yet a Heilant gentleman comes visitin' him regular — a fine figure o' a man in the kilt. They say this Heilander was his commandin' officer in the War and he set Charlie up in business here after it, because this Charlie saved his life: That's his wee shop wi' the black shutters — was you wantin' him aboot anything special?"

"Thanks", said Robert, "just wanted to know where he was — a friend of ours heard he was a great one for clock repairing".

The young couple smiled their thanks and crossed the road to the shop where the black shutters flanked dusty glass panes.

CLOSED announced a ticket stuck askew in the hat of a mechanical doll in the cluttered window. They looked into the gloom of the interior ...

June whispered, "A shadow — I saw a moving shadow".

"Let's walk down Holyrood way — don't want to act suspicious", said Robert.

What seemed to be about half an hour later (but the Canongate Tolbooth clock had moved its minute hand only seven times) Robert and June were back again in the vicinity of their brassware friend's shop, far enough away to pretend they did not see him standing at his shop door.

Suddenly Robert said in a voice charged with excitement, "Here she comes — don't look round — can you see Charlie's doorway reflected in this window? Aye, well let's just watch ..."

The red Herald swung in to a stop. Prendiss jumped out of the car and into the 'closed' shop whose door apparently opened on its own as he approached it. In no time he was out again, clutching a black case which he passed to his assistant.

Then with a roar the red car sped up the Canongate and disappeared from sight. "There goes our clues" said Robert. "One motor containing two possible crooks and a mysterious black case — all vanished".

He took a deep breath — "I'm going across to see this Charlie".

"Only if I come with you".

As they crossed the road, the mechanical doll in the window slowly raised one of its arms brushing the CLOSED notice stuck in its hat. The notice slowly slid to the base of the window. Nothing else moved.

*   *   *   *   *   *   *   *   *

Robert gripped the handle of the mysterious Charlie's door and turned it.

Locked.

"That was quick work", said Robert. He gave the door a shake. Nothing budged except for the mechanical doll in the window which slowly keeled over on its side covering the notice lying there marked CLOSED.

"Here's our friend from across the road" whispered June.

"Don't want to see him — let's get moving — down the way".

Without looking back they set off at a pace out of keeping with the warmth of the day, until they were out of sight in the towers of the Palace of Holyroodhouse again. They went into the restaurant at the Abbey Stand for coffee.

"I'll take you round Holyrood as planned, have lunch back here, and then June you'll have to try and contact your garage friend and see if he knows anything more about the photographer's moves. Your aunt expects you back mid-afternoon, doesn't she? Then I'll meet you again at seven for that theatre show.

"This is only Tuesday and the show-down, whatever it is, isn't until Thursday. Time is on our side ... I hope".

*   *   *   *   *   *   *   *   *

Tuesday near midnight. Robert Hart stood in a doorway not far from where June was staying. He had left her at her aunt's front door nearly an

hour before and waved as he turned the corner — apparently homeward bound. But, when out of sight, he began a circular move through the quiet district to come back on his tracks and station himself on the watch. He had promised that since she was spending Wednesday with relatives, he would 'phone her on Wednesday evening if he had found out anything more — but if not, they arranged to meet early on Thursday morning and had agreed if no nearer a solution then, they would go to the Police — unwillingly.

The reason for this vigil now was because June had seen her garage boy and been told that the red Herald had left for the Canongate that morning and was not due back until late — and the garage closed at midnight. To Robert's relief the car had arrived just before twelve o'clock and Robert awaited the driver and his assistant's appearance ...

Prendiss and sidekick came out of the garage, the younger man clutching the same black case. They walked across the road, turned right and vanished.

Robert ran quietly to the corner and began following them into one of the older streets of the New Town. He quickened his pace, taking from his pocket with a jingling flourish, his keys, as he noticed a sign, GUEST HOUSE in the offing and prayed that that was their destination. He was now only a few paces behind the two.

Prendiss, hearing his footsteps, turned to look — but Robert was apparently concentrating on disentangling one of his keys. When the two in front went up the steps of the guest house, Robert followed: and as Prendiss produced his latch key, Robert said: "Good evening — and well met — didn't want to disturb the whole house — this key's a bit temperamental at times".

Prendiss grunted.

Robert followed them in, closing the front door quietly behind him — immediately followed by an almost irresistible impulse to open it again and run along the street.

But he steeled himself to follow the two upstairs and when they went along the first floor corridor, he continued up to the next floor.

A door at the end had a sign with one letter missing; it read TO LET. Robert opened that door, locked it from the inside and hoped the loud thump-thump from his heart wasn't being heard all over the house.

All quiet ... then the sound of a door opening in the corridor below; then the opening and shutting of another door apparently underneath him.

Robert couldn't bear the inaction. The House was quiet as if all its occupants were deep in sleep — except whoever had walked along the corridor beneath him.

He slipped off his shoes, stuck them into the pockets of his jacket, opened the lavatory door and silently moved along the corridor and downstairs a step at a time until he could see through the bannister rails to the first floor corridor.

In the dim lighting, he concentrated all his attention on a bedroom door which had been left ajar, disclosing, in the brighter light of the bedroom interior what he guessed was the head and shoulders of Prendiss at that moment turning away from the light and grumpily pulling the sheets around him.

Robert now played his part in a series of unplanned inspired moves. Walking softly downstairs with the feeling that his hair was beginning to stand on end, he stopped at the partially opened doorway, gripped with finger and thumb round the inside edge of the yale-type lock, withdrew his fingers carefully, and walked back upstairs to his former position. Prendiss still had his back to the light. Robert waited ...

There was the noise of water flushing and taps gushing and then a pause. Prendiss's assistant appeared along the corridor, pushed open the door of the bedroom and pushed it shut with a click — the click coming from the lower door handle. Syd had naturally not noticed that, since leaving the bedroom, the upper and important lock had had its catch pushed up.

A strip of light showing under the bedroom door vanished. So far, action had kept down the tension but now he had nothing to do but force himself to wait. There was an awful moment when the outside door opened, softly shut ... and muffled footsteps went down to the basement.

When he could stand the waiting no longer, he crept down and stood listening at the bedroom door. A definite snore. From Prendiss? Was the younger one still awake? Robert had to take a chance — and wondered if he could say he had mistaken the room should he be challenged.

He slowly turned the lower placed handle of the door and then just as slowly pushed the door open. Pause ... He slipped through and pushed the door to again — and then stood trembling in the darkness. When his eyes accustomed to the change he could see the humped from of Prendiss who was snoring strongly and at the other side of the room the youth deathly still, lying on his back soundlessly asleep — Robert hoped. The faint light from the window was not sufficient to see any detail in the room and he knelt down on the well worn carpet and took a small torch from his inside pocket. The thin beam went round the room.

There it was. The black case, almost hidden behind an untidy chairful of clothes. Now, the worst part of all: to slide the case out to a position where he could see its contents.

This took time.

At last he had the case in a clear part of the carpet although uncomfortably near Prendiss's still snoring form. Robert slipped his torch back into his inside pocket and in near darkness felt round the sides of the case. He pressed a metal clasp and lifted the lid ... Slowly. Taking out the torch again he shone it into the case ... and saw the side of an old-fashioned whole-plate camera and a set of slides all neatly fitting in to a green baize-lined interior. Sick with disappointment he put out the torch and felt along the case for the means to close the lid ... As he groped, his fingers touched a small brass wheel on the side of the case ... and the sweat came out on his body as both camera and slides seemed to spring up as if hinged at one side of the case. The torch again ... It was no camera ...

Robert was now looking at a case with two lids: the outer one of ordinary black leather, the inner one a masterpiece of mahogany and brass made to look like the closed side of a camera complete with a set of slides all fitting snugly — but the whole affair no more than half an inch thick. And what he saw in the case itself had him staring in disbelief — hypnotised almost, and for a moment regardless of his surroundings.

Then with his mind racing, he began the feverish business of finding how to close the inner lid — to get the case back to its position on the floor by the chair — to crawl to the door, out and away into the clean night air and homeward bound.

The glorious feeling of having got away with his escapade! With the blood pounding away in his head he thought ... Just wait — just wait 'til I tell June what I've found, now I KNOW what it's all about.

As he hurried through the quiet streets, he was entirely oblivious to the amused glances of some late night strollers at the sight of a young man deep in thought — with his shoes stuck into his jacket pockets.

* * * * * * * * *

Thursday morning.

Robert Hart, bright-eyed with excitement, but dark-ringed about the eyes through lack of sleep, had June Ralston worried. He was a different lad from the one she had said goodnight to on Tuesday evening. He had not much to say: at the same time infuriatingly suggesting that he had a terrific lot to tell her. So why hadn't he phoned her on Wednesday then? Even when she asked how he had spent Wednesday, all he had come out with was he'd been posing as a tourist and asking questions; and never even asked how she had got on with her aunt and the visit to another relative. June was beginning to feel a huffiness coming on as they walked up the Mound and went through the gateway leading to the garden walk above the railway.

They climbed the path leading in dog-leg fashion to the entrance to the esplanade. They had gone a few yards up the slope when Robert looked round about him and suddenly said "Sit down a minute, June".

"Why, are you tired?"

"No. no, listen June ... that Prendiss character ... I think he's going to try and steal the Scottish Crown from the Castle". June sat down.

"You mean", swallowed June, pointing to the bulk of the Castle behind them, "the Crown is up there?".

Robert nodded. Then he told her of his Tuesday night adventure ...

"And there I was", he concluded, "staring into the big case in that pair's bedroom, and beautifully padded inside and underneath the double lid, was a replica of the Scottish Crown".

"But why should they want to do that — I mean they didn't look as if —"

"Oh, I've been thinking of nothing else since Tuesday night — well, that and you", and he smiled for the first time for a while, "I reckon they're in the pay of some fanatic who is giving them enough to make the risk worth while so that they can buzz off to South America or somewhere if needed. They must have official permission to photograph the Crown — forged letters from some crooked contact on the staff of an illustrated magazine abroad, maybe. And it all fits in, for Thursday night is when the Tattoo boys have the evening off: there will be peace to take the pictures without anyone else around except for an official or two. And that Charlie in the Canongate", Robert went on, "must have made the replica. Here's another bit that fits in I think — the Highland gent who visited Charlie, as that old boy at the shop door told us — what's the betting that Prendiss and the lad, after they collected the case as we saw, went to that gent's Highland home to let him see the works complete and get final instructions on delivery and that sort of thing — or maybe", said Robert slowing down at last, " excitement has been geting the better of me and I'm way off beam?"

There was silence between the two for a little ... and then June said: "No, I don't think so ... do you want to go to the Police now, Robert?"

He shook his head. June nodded, "Neither would I".

They stood up, looked at each other, slowly grinned, and then turning together, glanced up at the old Castle — the fortress guarding the Crown of Scotland — symbol of a kingdom.

* * * * * * * * *

Miss Euphemia Macower sat reading in her sitting room. At least she had a book before her. Miss Macower was thinking about June: about her preoccupied manner when they had been out together yesterday, and how she had kept out of her aunt's way for most of the day and had been meeting Robert outside — as apparently her intention was to do so again this evening. There was a mystery in the air as well as a thundery indication that the long warm spell was about to break down.

Miss Macower dismissed the thought that there was an elopement in the offing. Too soon. Far too soon, even allowing for the fast working of the young ones today, she thought.

The sound of June's footsteps coming downstairs. The girl looked round the door of the sitting room: "Goodnight, auntie, don't wait up, we're going to one of the late night shows".

"Goodnight dear", smiled Miss Macower. And immediately the front door closed, she grabbed her waterproof, an old tweed hat and a hefty walking stick from the hall stand.

Before June was at the end of the street, Miss Macower, in the early dimness of light brought on by an overcast sky, was on her trail.

June's aunt had read many thrillers where suspects were followed with ease. She found the reality different. She stopped in a doorway to watch the meeting of the young couple. Shadowing them was difficult in Leith Street and Princes Street, but the going was easier when they turned down Waverley Bridge and then right, up Market Street, crossing the Mound and on up Mound Place to Ramsay Lane.

When she saw them turn towards the Castle, she stoped for a breather ... then cautiously walked to the head of the lane and looked up Castlehill to the rear of the Royal Box and east stand on the esplanade. No sign. No one. She walked up to the head of the steps at Castle Wynd and looked down. Empty. Miss Macower, beginning to feel that the quarry had slipped away moved into the stand arena of the esplanade, like all theatres when performers are absent, eerie in the gloom.

The Castle floodlighting had not yet been switched on. There were only two lights apparent: one from the watchman's hut at the south east corner of the stands and one where the gateway over the drawbridge was illuminated; and against that were silhouetted June and Robert standing framed in the arch.

Miss Macower settled herself in the shadows at a corner of the stanos, and watched.

* * * * * * * * * *

Robert, feeling slightly daft, thumped a double knock for the second time on the door of the Castle ...

Studded boots sounded across cobbles: the smaller door set into the main gateway opened. Robert said: "I wish to speak to the guard commander, please".

"What aboot, sir?" queried the small but stocky kilted one, eyeing June with favour.

"Private and official business".

"Jist a minute" — and the kilted one disappeared — to be replaced in the doorway by a taller version with two stripes who said, politely but warily: "Good evening, sir, can I help you?"

"Yes, I've reason to believe a photographer is coming here shortly to take pictures inside the Castle. I have information which I think means that his car should be searched before he gets any further than this entrance".

"What kind of information?" asked the corporal.

"Sorry, the less people know about that, the better — all I ask is that you —"

"Now lissen, son, maybe there is a photographer coming and maybe I've already got papers as proof of identity and permission to —"

"They're faked I'll bet. Please listen to me. All I ask is that you should search the car".

"Then we find nothing and the bloke complains and I'm up on a charge and all because you come up and ..." The corporal took his eyes off June to look directly at Robert and continued: "You know what? I think you're one o' thae students up to some damned stupid stunt o' some kind — off you go son, or would you prefer being arrested?"

Robert, keeping his temper with difficulty, took a calculating look at the soldier. "Come on, June", he said, and turned on his heel.

They walked in silence until they heard the bang of the Castle door behind them.

"You gave up easily, Robert?"

"Not given up. But that's hopeless there. I expected it might be. But I've got an alternative plan".

As they left the esplanade, Robert said: "I'm going in another way. Believe me it's OK. You must trust me"

"Only if I go with you".

"This time, NO. This is a little mountaineering job. Honest, it's safe, and you must go home please, and wait until ..."

"This time, NO". They stopped and faced each other.

"Well", said Robert, "will you promise to go back and stay near the watchman on the esplanade? Chat with him. I really won't be long after Prendiss arrives according to the time I found out about yesterday. But I'd rather you went home".

"I won't go home, but all right I'll stay on the esplanade — it'll be horrible, with me there and you doing some risky climb".

Robert refused further details on his scheme while they returned down Ramsay Lane to where the railings curve into Mound Place.

Looking round to see that no-one watched, Robert drew himself up to the railings top and jumped down on to the garden side.

"Won't be long, June" and turned to go. But June said "Robert". He turned back. She stood on tip toe on the stonework at the base of the railings.

She kissed him in an entirely different way from that goodnight peck on the cheek of Tuesday evening. "Good luck, Robert!"

Robert said nothing and disappeared into the dusk of the garden slopes — all set now to fight dragons, let alone criminal cameramen.

*   *   *   *   *   *   *   *   *   *

As Robert disappeared in the direction of the Castle rock, June, feeling suddenly very much all alone, walked back up Ramsay Lane and was confronted by an elderly lady at the entrance to Ramsay Garden. Said the elderly lady: "Well, miss, and what have you to say for yourself and where has Robert gone?"

"Auntie! What are you doing here? How did you get to — "

"*I'm* asking the questions June; come on, what's it all about?"

"Please come back to the esplanade, first, *please.*"

Miss Macower, seing the anxious expression on her niece's face, said, "Very well, we'll go back to the esplanade. We'll ... em ... tell the watchman that my officer nephew is coming out of the Castle shortly, on leave, and we're here to surprise him. And then we'll sit beyond earshot of the man and you'll tell me all about it".

* * * * * * * * * *

The Castle floodlighting came on as Robert, having raced across the slope, stood under the shadow of the rock where the garden path widens below the Argyll Tower. Down below, Princes Street glittered; dancing was in full swing in front of the bandstand in the gardens. Directly above him, like a giant outthrust knee, a buttress, ivy-covered, seemed to be supporting the Tower above. Robert had to get up the rock, up and over that buttress and on to the flat roof by the inner roadway and then drop down to the portcullis gate of the Argyll Tower.

He began to climb.

The band in Princes Street gardens was playing a care-free melody. The young man fighting his way through ivy-covered and ancient stonework felt anything but care-free. The ascent was taking longer than expected ...

The sound of a car coming up the roadway within the Castle ...

The red Herald?

Steady progress brought him at last onto the flat roof where he crouched while recovering his breath; and then, checking that no-one was in sight, he went down by the conveniently bracketed lead rain pipe to the causeway. Another pause under the portcullis of the Tower, then through the archway and up the long stairs (praying he'd not meet someone coming down).

Now he was crouching in sight of the Scottish National War Memorial.

There was a mutter of thunder following a lurid glow from lightning masked behind cumulus cloud; then silence again. It was a measure of the tension being suffered by Robert that when the first big rain drop spat on to the back of his outstretched hand, he started nervously. Then he was again running, crouched low, to the entrance to Crown Square, by which time the rain had begun in earnest.

The Square was deserted.

The room containing the Regalia was a blaze of light. A burst of laughter. Prendiss making a joke? He must have nerve, thought Robert as he ran along to where the Herald was parked and crept up a step or two of the short turret stair and then lowered himself full length so that his head, hidden in shadow, was level with the floor; inside, a group of men stood beyond the showcase containing the Regalia: a soldier with fixed bayonet, two officials, Prendiss and Syd his assistant. All this seen through the heavy metal grill closed across the opening of the doorway — the door itself, being left open because of the airless heat of the evening.

The room was untidy with photographic equipment. The Crown only, had been taken from the showcase and placed on a small velvet-draped dais no more than a foot or so from the ground.

"Now for the close-up looking down view, gentlemen". Prendiss contracted the legs of the camera stand and focused ... Then looked round ... "What I want now is extra light reflected on the shadowed side. Bring over the old camera case with the spare whole-plate, Syd. That's it. Now we'll place it so and open the lid".

The black camera case was now on the floor beside the small dais supporting the Crown. Its open lid showing the (apparent) side and slides of a camera of the old type in mahogany and brass.

"Now", said Prendiss, "something white to put into the inside of the open lid to reflect the flash". He bent down and took a white card lettered on one side from a brief case. "This'll do", and he jammed it into the inside of the black lid of the camera case ... "a bit of improvisation, gentlemen ... just hold the card lightly by your finger tips in that position, Syd".

Then he continued: "Have a look at this, gentlemen. I think I'll have it patented. Something I made up myself". He then held out a large basin-shaped lamp shade with a powerful bulb in the centre and on the inside of the shade a mosaic of small mirrors.

"These little mirrors are faceted to concentrate the light so that I can turn the lamp down to the smallest aperture and still get, in very close-up, a surprising depth of focus".

Beads of sweat sprang out on Prendiss's brow as he held out the lamp towards the three men to show them the inside.

"NOTE THE REFLECTOR, GENTLEMEN" — and a vivid glare of intense white light lit the room like a lightning flash.

Robert remembered the phrase Prendiss had given as the cue for action, overheard from the balcony on the Nelson column — and had instinctively shut his eyes at the all important moment. As he opened them again he saw Syd, with nerveless hands, completing a well rehearsed move of taking the Crown from its dais, laying it on the floor, pressing the wheel to raise the inner lid of the black case, taking out the replica of the crown, placing it on the dais, inserting the real Crown in the box and closing the inner lid — all in a matter of ten seconds — while confusion reigned in the room with Prendiss profusely apologising, saying that the trigger was much too sensitive, that he wished he'd a fiver for every time the flashlight had temporarily blinded him too — and went on apologising until the two disgruntled officials and the soldier began to see properly again.

"Oh dear, dear, I'm sorry about all that", said the photographer for about the tenth time, "But no real harm done, eh? — and you all right Syd?"

Syd, kneeling by the black case with his hands holding the lid in position for the photograph, nodded and smiled for the first time since coming to Edinburgh.

For the sake of appearances, Prendiss now had to stay and actually take more pictures.

Robert, putting himself in the officials' place, thought: what would be their reaction if a very dishevelled young man with a large tear down his trousers showing a bloodied knee and with hands and face scratched and blackened with earth and rubble shouted through the grill that the photographer had just stolen the Crown?.

No, it wouldn't do.

I'll try my corporal friend, thought Robert and he ran for the stairs and so down under the Argyll arch again and on to the guard room at the entrance gate. He battered on the guard room door and then shoved it open without ceremony, appearing among the half-sleeping warriors including the corporal who, not sure if he was seeing things, managed to blurt out: "YOU again!". He made a grab at Robert who, bloodied, wet, mucky and almost out of breath, gasped, "Turn out the guard, corporal, PLEASE turn out the guard".

It was the members of the guard themselves, sensing all this as a diversion to pass the weary hours — particularly as the rain had suddenly stopped — who persuaded the corporal to give Robert a hearing.

The young man finished a brief speech with: "I can't tell you what it is all about, but there is a black case in the photographer's car, and there is something now in that case that could cause a nationwide sensation — and honestly, corporal, I'd hate to be you if this camera-type criminal got away with it".

In the silence that followed that plea, the guard commander looked Robert in the eye ... then straightening his belt and adjusting his bonnet, strode to the door, swung round and bawled: "GUARD TURN OUT!"

* * * * * * * * * *

Prendiss did not like the sight of a line of soldiers with fixed bayonets standing across the cobbled space before the firmly closed doors by the drawbridge as he drove down from the Castle heights.

The corporal held out a hand. Prendiss, slowing up, opened the side window and said: "What's all this about, soldier, we're in something of a hurry y'know".

"Routine sir, just routine, won't be a minute, got to search the car".

"But this is nonsense, all we've been concerned with is —"

"Excuse me, sir", cut in the corporal guard commander as he signalled to two of his men. One lifted a cloth from the rear seats and shone his torch on the equipment. The key for the boot of the car was grudgingly given, while Prendiss kept revving the engine impatiently. Nothing in the boot. The corporal looked murderously at Robert — but Robert whispered:

"Something in the front seat, the lad's legs look awkwardly high, could be he's got a case under them, but watch —"

At that precise moment a distraction in the form of a loud blare from a motor horn came from the outer side of the drawbridge.

"Geez", said one of the guard reverently — "The Colonel" — and trotted to the big doors, and, almost before he had both sides open, the Colonel's car was barging in. The Colonel peering through his windscreen saw a line of soldiers, one scruffy youth and a red car. The colonel slowed down and swung to the right. Prendiss saw his chance and shot forward, sending the soldier who was about to close the doors flying back against the wall. Beyond the drawbridge, he narrowly missed the guard at the sentry box. In seconds, Prendiss was approaching the east end of the esplanade at lunatic speed followed by a line of soldiers led by Robert and the corporal, with Robert shouting 'STOP THE CAR, JUNE, STOP THE CAR!"

It was Miss Macower, however, who went into action as the red Herald reached the opening leading off the esplanade. To June's alarm, her aunt walked forward as if to meet the car in its mad rush, spray flying from its wheels.

*   *   *   *   *   *   *   *   *

Miss Macower swung her hefty walking stick at the oncoming car. The stick hit the windscreen smack in front of the driver who instinctively jerked the steering wheel — and the surface of the esplanade, newly soaked after the long drought, did the rest.

The car skidded into the wall supporting the railings adjoining the houses of Ramsay Garden with a loud crash — Prendiss slumped over the wheel. But Syd was out, over the railings and away into the darkness of the garden slopes below — clutching the black case.

Syd, criminal assistant to the criminal cameraman, went slithering down through the wet grass of the garden slope towards the railway bridge behind the bandstand.

Like a rat he had chosen the darkness, although he had no idea what he meant to do next. Nor was he aware that he was travelling in the general direction of the Perthshire Highlands to where, if all had gone well, he and his boss would have been making their second visit to a Jacobite fanatic who believed himself to be the last of the line of the Royal Stewarts and to whom they had planned to deliver the stolen Crown of Scotland.

The unlawful bearer of that Crown stumbled on to the railway bridge and became aware at one and the same time, that a wooden gate was fastened across the far end of it and that a bedraggled figure was following him across. As Syd made a desperate run and clambered onto and almost over the gate, Robert made a flying tackle at him and both rolled back on to the footway of the bridge.

A struggle in the dark, silent except for the gasping breaths of the two young men — then Syd shook himself free and made another dive for the gate.

Again, Robert held him and almost threw him back on to the footway with what was all but the remainder of his strength. Then as his opponent jumped up and came at him, Robert dropped flat to escape the swinging kick, and hunching his shoulders drove himself up hard against the under-side of the temporarily off-balanced enemy.

Syd described a backward curve, accompanied by a yell, hit his head against the cast-iron sides of the bridge and lay still.

"Here they are", bawled a voice and a trio of soldiers, one of them the corporal with a torch, ran on to the bridge.

Robert, speechless, pointed to Syd who was roughly jerked to his feet by two of the men. Then Robert, having recovered some breath, said: "The case. The black case. Where is it? Shine your torch down on the railway line".

Nothing there on either side. Had a train passed during the fight? He couldn't remember. Then he staggered to the wooden gate and looked over. "It's here! He must have chucked it over before trying to get across the gate, same as he must have thrown it over the railings up at the esplanade. Could one of you get it? I don't think I've got the strength".

The corporal himself vaulted over and bent down at the black case.

"For Pete's sake, don't touch any of those brass fittings at the side", said Robert — "inside it's cushioned against being thrown about, but there's a wheel at the side that, if it was turned ... well ..."

The corporal, looking at Robert with respect, gingerly handed the case across.

A pre-arranged signal with the torch to the esplanade, then a little pro-cession went slowly up the garden slope above the railway. In the rear, a sorry cameraman's assistant between two kilted figures and in front, Robert clasping the black case, shuffling wearily beside the corporal who said: "Sorry about turnin' you away up there".

"O.K. would have done the same myself".

"Lissen, pal, you a boffin's assistant or something? — and what's IN the bloody box, just looks like an old camera case to me".

"Well, as I said up at the guard room" and Robert stopped for breath and also to do a bit of quick thinking ... "what's in that case could have caused a nationwide sensation ... it would have been better from the crooks' point of view now, if it had been left in the Castle".

"Then", said the corporal foreseeing himself the centre of barrrack room attention later, "They must never have had the chance of doin' the damage up there that they planned — and these two blokes were in the pay of what we call a foreign power — and everybody kens what that means?"

"That's about it", nodded a weary but smiling Robert.

And so the story went round the Castle garrison that somebody or something had narrowly escaped a big blow up — thanks to the guard com-mander at the gate.

*　*　*　*　*　*　*　*　*

Only Miss Macower, June, the Colonel, Robert — and a very surprised and thankful official of the two in the Crown room when the flash went off, knew what had actually happened, and that no harm had come to the Crown. Only they knew the truth and had good reason all, to keep it to themselves.

Of course there were another four involved: Prendiss was treated in the Castle hospital and when recovered, he and his assistant the sorry Syd, also having been temporarily resident within, were escorted across the Border and set free, on condition that they kept quiet about the whole affair — with the hint that Scotland Yard was tipped off to keep an eye on them. The same applied to Canongate Charlie who left the Royal Mile very suddenly. And finally, the Colonel, who had known the Jacobite fanatic Laird in Perthshire, in the happier days when they were both young subalterns, went to see him privately. No prosecution there either.

* * * * * * * * *

Friday evening. The thundery showers had released Edinburgh from the long heat wave, and a fresh, clear gloaming light hung above the Castle as the Mounted Band of the Household Cavalry, led by the old Drum Horse, left the arena of the Tattoo.

There was silence for a moment after the applause, broken only by the muted sound of hooves clattering down Castlehill.

The floodlights then swung back to the Castle drawbridge ... Beyond, could be heard faint wild music gradually becoming louder and louder as the great doors of the Castle opened in unison and on came the massed Pipes and Drums of the Scottish regiments, fanning out in strict formation then coming down the esplanade in a glitter of shining ornament to the swing of the tartan and the fierce pulsing beat of the drums ...

There had been some last minute re-arrangements to allow four seats in the front row of the Royal box to be kept specially. In them now, sat Miss Macower with the Colonel and June with Robert.

As the line of Drum Majors approached the foot of the esplanade, Miss Macower glanced sideways at the young couple. Robert, in a new suit and gallantly scarred a bit about the face, sat stolidly looking ahead, the muscles of his jaw working slightly. June's eyes shone bright — the brighter for the hint of a tear; her left hand was firmly — very firmly, clasped in Robert's right. Miss Macower noticed this too and nodding her head in satisfaction to herself, turned her eyes again to the brave spectacle before her on the esplanade.

Miss Macower was well content.

A Clansman at Culloden

By RENNIE McOWAN

I was happy although exhausted that night I lay in the dark in the heather and the sharp prong of my targe and the handle of my dirk kept sticking into my side when I tried to snatch some sleep.

I wrapped myself more tightly in my Cameron war plaid and tried to doze until the order we had all been waiting for would be given to us. By that time you could have said that we were desperate men because there were thousands of us lying hidden in the heather, occasionally muttering as rain and sleet soaked the moor and the April wind which still had the taste of winter snow and ice about it worked its way through the hollows of the peat hags and set the birches and the alders quivering on a small mound where our chiefs sat in a small group quietly conversing.

All around were the big Highland hills still white with snow and as I shifted my sword to get a more comfortable sleeping position I wondered how many of us by nightfall the next day would still see the snow on the hills and smell the scent of wet birch and heather after rain.

Just before I drifted off to sleep I thought of these months that had passed, of how we had marched in ranks to join the Prince and the other Jacobite chiefs at Glenfinnan.

We were late in arriving and some of the men laughed to themselves that we had done that by design because by the time the Cameron contingents arrived at the mustering place the MacDonalds and Stewarts had gathered and our absence had been noticed and I think it could have truthfully been said that there would have been no rising if our chief, Locheil, had not called us out.

Anyway, whether I was to be alive or dead tomorrow, I remembered it well, that great day when our piper crested the brae and we followed on behind him, our weapons shining, our plaids flapping in the breeze and we could see all the faces down below looking towards us and cheering broke out as we tramped downhill and everyone knew that the Rising was now a reality.

I've slept in a lot of odd places since then, lying among rushes at Gladsmuir just before our first battle when we swept General Cope's men from the field and and in barns and sheds and behind walls when we made our long march into England only to find that the French had not landed, the English Jacobites did not rush to join us, and with London almost within our grasp our leaders felt that we should return to the Highlands and there try and capture the hated Hanoverian force and then, joined by other clans, we would come again in the Spring.

I remember, too, falling asleep through exhaustion during the retreat from Clifton, in the north of England, when one of the Glengarry Mac-Donalds who had fought a disciplined rearguard action kicked me to my feet and made me march on when all I wanted to do was to fall down and sleep.

Most men find it hard to sleep before a battle and that was certainly true at Falkirk when the Hanoverian army caught up with us and even brought their own hangmen to execute those of us who would become prisoners of war, but we showed them.

We were not beaten yet and under our great military commander, General Lord George Murray, we sent them packing yet again and I can remember to this day seeing some of the MacDonald clansmen lying flat on the heather as the dragoons thundered towards them and then nimbly wriggling sideways to avoid the hooves as the horses galloped over them and then, with one blow, bringing down both horse and rider. It takes great courage and timing to do that and it was something I could never manage myself, but I think I did well enough when the charge was ordered and the blood sprang to the head and we rushed towards the enemy.

All this went through my mind as I tried to sleep because another battle was upon us and this time we were not in such good heart.

Many of the men were very tired and some had gone back to their own glens to see to the safety of their families because reports had come in that the Hanoverian soldiers and their Campbell allies had been burning the homesteads in some of the land owned by clans who had joined the Prince.

I am sorry to say that our leaders had begun to fall out with one another at this stage over what should be done next and we had sent sizeable contingents of the army, including the MacPhersons, into other areas.

That was necessary to deal with groups of the enemy but it weakened our main army. We were all accustomed to living off nothing more than oatmeal at this stage but even that was beginning to run out and many of the men were hungry.

We were not at our best to fight a pitched battle but as I had joined in one of our charges three times now and had seen us victorious each time I thought that we could still do it again.

But then came news of a different kind. General Cumberland, with a large army, was encamped not far from us and our chief and others decided we would attack his camp at night. The more we thought about it, the more we all felt the idea had our enthusiasm because we knew that our rush would take us past the sentries and in among the tents before Cumberland's men had time to grab their arms. We knew from our patrols that he was not certain where we were and would probably not expect such an attack.

All this passed through my mind as I tried to sleep, but I needn't have bothered because suddenly a figure in a feathered bonnet was bending over me and I was being told to pick up my weapons and to quietly follow the man in front of me until I got further orders.

I think I will remember that night forever.

By this time we were all hardened campaigners and, in the pale light of the moon which occasionally flickered through the dark clouds, I could see long lines of men creeping forward, their weapons hidden inside their plaids so that no gleam would catch a sentry's eye, their deer-hide footwear making no sound in the heather and their targes slung on their backs.

From all over the moor they came and I think we must have had at least a couple of thousand men and I learned later that some others had been held back as a reserve force.

Every now and then a whisper would come down the line and the man in front of me would turn round and say: "We've to halt until further orders. There's to be no talking and no movement" and I remember crouching anxiously there, the sweat chilling on me in the night wind, until another whisper came down the line and we were ordered to slip forward once more.

Ahead of us in the dark I could see the black outline of the crest of the moor and we were halted just below it and asked to spread out sideways in long lines, again with no talking and no noise and by this time we had one or two stragglers because, as I said, some of the men were very hungry. Then we were ordered forward to just below the crest.

We learned in detail later what had happened, how Lord George Murray had carefully checked out the enemy's camp and led us to the point where sentries were less numerous and the camp at its most vulnerable because below the crest lay a wide burn and then grassy flat ground and moorland on which were pitched hundreds of tents, with the mouth of the camp, so to speak, at the far side around which had been built makeshift barriers on which fieldpieces had been mounted.

The Hanoverian army had used the high ground that we had crossed as a kind of wall behind them and they did not expect a Highland rush from that side.

I suppose all of the sentries near the crest were killed. All I know is that I saw the body of one of them just below the crest and could make out his red coat and crossbelts in the dim light and standing over him was one of our lads with a dirk in his hand.

Then our commanders hurried along the line, again whispering more orders. We were to charge over the crest, down the other side, across the burn, through the tents, thereby taking the gunners and the sentries at the other side in the rear. We were not to stop for our own wounded. We were not to stop for anything! Every figure coming out of a tent was to be treated as an enemy and cut down.

We were to be careful that in the dark we did not accidentally shoot or stab any of our own men and were instructed that once the charge reached the far side of the camp orders would be given for our men to halt, rally and charge back through the camp a second time. We were told that other parties had been sent further down the strath to cut off fugitives and to warn us of any unexpected reinforcements.

I remember it still, the pacing sentries in the gloom below, the stacks of arms, the white tents, the tethered horses, little pennons flying from some of the tents showing where officers slept and groups of soldiers sitting chatting round huge fires while others lay sleeping on the ground, their arms beside them.

I can't say I can remember too much about what happened next because it all passed so quickly and yet it must have been upwards of an hour.

By that time in the campaign we were fighting mad, and when the order to charge came we went over the crest and down the slope like stags coming down a hillside, roaring our heads off in our clan slogan: "O sons of dogs, come here and I will give you flesh!'

On each side of us, Stewarts and MacDonalds and MacLachlans and others all did the same and although our army was organised by this time into proper regiments, nevertheless it was second nature for most of us to fight as a clan body.

We were across the stream in seconds and in among them! We slashed at the guy-ropes of tents bringing them down, we stabbed at the occupants through the canvas, all around there were screams and shouts and our pipers on the ridge behind played the old war tunes.

I remember men looming up in front of me and cutting them down like nettles and rushing on only to find others doing the same and once I had to take a blow from a musket butt on my targe and I was knocked to the ground by another soldier, but some of the MacDonalds running forward on my right dealt with them and I was able to get up again and run on and so it went on until we were in among the cannon and cutting down the gunners in a hugh melee of shouting and cursing men.

It became increasingly difficult to spot friend from foe in the half-dark and shouts from our leaders and the sound of the pipes brought most of us together at the far side of the camp and we could partly see and hear little knots of the enemy running downstream and clambering out of the base of the strath and we left them to be dealt with by our patrols and by our reserve force.

By this time some of the Hanoverian soldiers had managed to load muskets or to fix bayonts and they were forming defensive groups and one volley from them into the darkness brough down some men near me, but again the orders to charge were given and we crashed back again through the tents and there was nothing for it, but to cut and slash and parry until some of our stragglers got up on the crest of the ridge with a piper and succeeded in making such a racket that the enemy thought another battle force had arrived and they began to surrender.

As the light improved we saw that we had won a crushing victory. A Highland broadsword wielded by experienced men can wreak dreadful havoc and the floor of the strath was littered with corpses and with wounded men. Locheil gave orders that the prisoners were to be gathered together at one side and there were many of these. The only sad bit for us was that Cumberland and some of his staff had escaped and they may have been in one of the groups that we heard clattering down the glen.

As the early morning light came in we counted our booty and our losses. We did not have many killed but we did have a fair number of wounded, some, I am sorry to say, as a result of blows from their comrades in the half-dark and before identity could be established. The booty was very great and we captured much neded supplies, cheese, biscuits, flour and oatmeal, plus bottles of wine and other liquor which soon vanished.

We set out to spike the cannon so that they could not be used again and we broke all the muskets that we could and we piled all their ammunition that we did not need for ourselves into a huge heap and then, having marched all the men and horses back from it for about a mile, we lit a trail of gunpowder and up it went in an enormous roar that could have been heard in Inverness.

Ah, that was a great night! We had thrashed our enemy yet again and surely now, well-armed and provisioned once again, we had gained time.

Surely now the French would come and the other clans would rise and more and more men would see that our Prince, Tearlath, was the rightful possessor of the throne of Britain.

My tired mind tried to grasp all this and sleep came and went and all of a sudden I felt a great chill come over my body and a great weariness possessed my spirit. I started when a hand was placed on my shoulder and I saw a man's face in a feathered bonnet bend over mine in the early hours of the morning and say: "Wake up, lad! Wake up! They're here! They're here!"

And I realised that I was not on a dark moor but lying sleeping in heather alongside the great grey walls of Ruthven Barracks in Badenoch which we had captured earlier in the campaign and all around me were men from several clans, thousands of them, still with their weapons but tired and weary-looking.

Close by I could see other Highlanders who looked like the MacPhersons and I was surprised because I knew that they had been campaigning elsewhwere.

I was exhausted because a few days before I had taken part in that last desperate charge of the clans on Culloden Moor, when we were shot at and cut down by grapeshot and cannon fire for what seemed like hours before the men could stand it no longer and charged the Hanoverian ranks. It was a mistake and badly timed and hundreds fell dead but we smashed through their front line and might well have done the same to the second but we were outnumbered and exhausted and had to leave the field.

Our cause seemed lost and the remnants of our army were urged to make for Ruthven Barracks which was to be the new rallying point.

Despite that terrible day on Culloden Moor and the loss of so many dear friends I could see that we were still a force to be reckoned with because contingents of our army had been elsewhere under orders when Culloden was fought and had now returned. Tired though I was my spirits rose when I realised that we now had more men at Ruthven than we were able to muster at Culloden and the fight could go on.

Even over the years I cannot bear to tell without weeping what happened next.

Our leaders were no longer united, the Prince bade us return to our homes and look to our own safety and that of our families and he then left to go into hiding and eventual exile.

Many of the men wept and some shouted protests at him and some said they would fight on as guerillas.

As for me, I sat with my head on my knees, sick with the knowledge and the memory that the real night-attack on Cumberland's camp had been cancelled and what I had seen and felt had only been the kind of dream exhausted men have at times of tension and danger.

Many a time in future years, wielding a sword in other lands for other men's causes, I thought of that dream and its vivid memories.

It was a dream that could very easily have been reality and, if so, the story of the Highlands and of my country would have been very, very different.

Would that it had been so!

The Sinking of John McDougall

BY JOHN BONNER

At the beginning of the nineteenth century, Glasgow had a population of around 100,000. The city was in the throes of industrial revolution, progressing gradually towards establishing its worldwide reputation for shipbuilding and engineering that would last for more than 150 years. As the city expanded, its population grew enormously, swelled by businessmen, tradesmen, tinkers and quick-witted opportunists from all over Scotland and the north of England.

Among the batch of new arrivals in 1813 was a young man named John McDougall. Rothesay-born, he had an impressive physique, standing over six feet, with a bull-neck and powerful shoulders and arms. His ruddy complexion and untidy red hair gave the initial impression of low intellect, but the truth was far from that. Coming from a family of gypsies who travelled around the West, he had resolved in his early teens to leave that life behind him at the first opportunity, and in 1802, he made the break and moved to Campbeltown.

Work was plentiful and young John frequently changed his employment, always with the purpose of improving his working conditions and prospects. By 1806, in his mid-twenties, he had elevated himself to the secure and prosperous position of shipping agent for the packet boats which sailed between Campbeltown and the Broomielaw. In the next two years, he prospered even more when he bought himself into partnership with a consortium of businessmen who were shipping herring to Glasgow.

By 1810, he was part-owner of a small steamer which transported goods to the Kyles of Bute.

In less than a decade, McDougall, employing considerable ingenuity and a dogged determination to succeed had totally transformed his lifestyle. Although by many standards he was now a wealthy man, highly respected by neighbours, local councillors and businessmen, his ambitions were far from sated. He wanted further wealth and power and the only place he could achieve this, he decided, was in Glasgow. In 1813, he sold all his business interests and left Campbeltown for the last time.

Once established in the city, McDougall quickly introduced himself to various business acquaintances and shipping agents with the intention of investing part or all of his considerable wealth in some promising undertaking. Within three months, he had become part-owner of a sloop, the *Mary,* and a brigantine, the *Friends.*

From temporary lodgings he moved to a fashionable house in Jamaica Street, and then rented modern business premises in St Enoch Square where he set about procuring business for his vessels. Along with his two partners, he spent every working day badgering and cajoling owners and traders to use the *Mary* and *Friends* to transport their goods. McDougall always insisted on insuring his vessels before even taking the cargo aboard. It was noted with some surprise and pleasure by the Glasgow underwriters that McDougall selected very large, not to say excessive, insurance coverage.

For the first 18 months, the new enterprise progressed at a sedate rather than brisk pace, offering encouragement and promise, but falling well short of McDougall's impatient hopes and unrealistic expectations. It became necessary, therefore, to bring forward the first stage of what was originally intended as an alternative, but nevertheless carefully-calculated scheme.

At the beginning of 1814, McDougall, along with one of his partners, James Menzies, purchased a small sailing vessel and used it to ship salt herring to The Netherlands. It was a profitable exercise, but not of a scale to satisfy McDougall who, always with an ulterior motive in mind, once again over-insured. A few months later, the craft "foundered" in the North Sea. The crew took to a lifeboat and reported in detail the "unfortunate" loss. Glasgow underwriters duly and without fuss paid out, and the comparative ease and simplicity of the transaction was all the encouragement McDougall needed to progress further with his criminal career.

With the first stage of the exercise successfully completed, he was now prepared to undertake the biggest risk of his life. Success in the fraudulent venture he had in mind would bring wealth and security for life. Failure would mean, at best, bankruptcy and ruin, and at worst almost certain death on the gallows.

First, he had to gather round him men who had certain qualifications: they had to be registered seamen, capable at their job, but at the same time receptive to an illegal proposition; they had to have the nerve and ability to carry out their unlawful task; and, more important than anything, they had to be able to keep their mouths shut after the job was completed. He decided against using any of the crew from the previous venture, reasoning that another shipping loss involving the same owners and men might create suspicion among the insurance companies.

After weeks of discreet questioning by himself and his partner James Menzies, McDougall decided to approach Captain Robert Duncan, a slight business acquaintance who was also an experienced seaman. Most important of all, Duncan was in dire need of cash to settle a pressing debt regarding the purchase of a large quantity of fishing equipment.

McDougall found out that Duncan frequented an alehouse near Glasgow Cross, and he decided to arrange an "accidental" meeting there. Duncan later described how McDougall spoke to him outside the bar.

"I was surprised at the warmth of Mr McDougall's greeting", he recounted. "And even more so when he accompanied me inside to the bar, for I wasn't aware that he took a drink. He ordered and paid for some drinks, but I noticed that he barely touched his. After half an hour he told me he would like to discuss some business with me in confidence ...

"Without revealing any details, he gradually gave me the idea that the business arrangement he had in mind was not legal ... I wouldn't commit myself unless he told me exactly what he wanted me to do ... It was then that he told me he owned the brigantine *Friends* and was losing money on it.

"The only way he could regain his losses was if the vessel sank. I was offered the position as Master of the vessel and it was made clear to me that I would be responsible for the sinking of the *Friends* when it sailed for Europe in June. How and where this was to be done was left up to me. For my part in the plan I was promised the sum of £100 when I returned to Glasgow, and if everything went successfully I was told I would be paid an additional sum when the insurance was recovered. McDougall also mentioned the opportunity of me being in charge of a larger vessel he was thinking of purchasing, and even hinted at the possibility of a future partnership. To all this I agreed".

Shortly afterwards, McDougall and James Menzies hired a seaman named Daniel Bannatyne as First Mate on the *Friends* and offered him a financial deal to act in collusion with Duncan. Three other seamen were recruited, but since their co-operation in the fraud was not necessary, they were hired in the normal way. The next stop for McDougall was to notify merchants by means of advertising in the Press that the *Friends* would be sailing for Hamburg in June and that there was room on board for cargo. The third member of the business partnership, John McGregor, was totally unaware of what his two partners were scheming.

McDougall, Menzies, Duncan and Bannatyne met many times in the following weeks, usually in the same alehouse, in an attempt to perfect

Water gushes through the hole he had bored

their plan, discussing problems that might arise and any potential pitfalls and how to cope with them. Two important points were covered in great detail at that time. The first was by the two owners that every item of cargo put aboard the *Friends* at Glasgow would be unloaded again when the vessel backtracked up the Forth and Clyde Canal to Port Dundas, in the city. The goods would then be re-shipped and re-sold at a later date. The second point covered was the suggestion by Captain Duncan that the most effective way of sinking the vessel was to drill holes in her bottom. His solution was to bore "between three and six holes" using an auger about one and a half inches in diameter.

By mid-June when *Friends* sailed into Port Dundas she was fully laden, having taken on cargo at Greenock and Port Glasgow. Once berthed, all goods were removed to a large warehouse rented by McDougall for the purpose. Only the four conspirators did the unloading, and once that was achieved they were joined by the other three members of the crew. The vessel's route took her back to the River Clyde, and through the Forth & Clyde Canal. She docked one night at Leith then headed out into the North Sea.

When the vessel was 140 miles off the Danish coast and the unsuspecting crew were about their duties, Duncan and Bannatyne slipped below. As Duncan began boring, Bannatyne was making adjustments to the water pump which was compulsory on every vessel. When the drill had almost completed the first hole, a high-pitched hiss and powerful spray preceded a surging jet of water which gushed into the hold. A second hole was drilled about three feet away, then a third and fourth before the two men quickly went up on deck. They waited a few minutes then alerted the crew that the ship was taking water. The three seamen rushed below and immediately began operating the crude pump, rendered useless by Bannatyne. As the North Sea poured in and the prospects of keeping the *Friends* afloat became hopeless, Captain Duncan ordered the vessel to be abandoned. The five men took to the lifeboat and within an hour were picked up by a Danish fishing vessel which put them ashore at Warde, in Denmark. There, magistrates took a statement from each man and these were sealed and forwarded to Glasgow.

At the beginning of July, the crew of the *Friends* returned home and gave McDougall an account of how his vessel had been lost. He in turn registered his claim for compensation with the insurance companies, and then prepared for the worst part of the whole operation — waiting while the matter was investigated.

When this was completed and nothing irregular discovered, the decision of the underwriters to pay came as an immense relief to McDougall. The vessel was officially registered as lost "due to stress of weather".

After a suitable period had elapsed, the goods abstracted at Port Dundas, mainly coffee, cocoa and cloth, were despatched and sold in England and Ireland. Since they had cost the conspirators nothing, the proceeds were clear profit. The entire operation could hardly have gone better. Within six months of the *Friends* being lost, McDougall and, to a lesser extent, Menzies, had in their possession the insurance money and the cash for the stolen goods, a total of over £18,000. It was the perfect crime — if only those involved could be trusted to remain silent.

For the next three years, McDougall reverted to the role of successful, respectable and legitimate businessman. Although he retained his connections with John McGregor and James Menzies in the ownership of the sloop, *Mary*, it was mainly on his own that he undertook any further commitments.

There was no doubt that McDougall's status in the eyes of city businessmen rose considerably in those years. He wined and dined in Glasgow's finest establishments; furnished his home with the grandest and most sought-after items; and, in 1818, ordered work to start on a mansion-style house on the Isle of Bute.

With what many people considered to be an almost indecent display of wealth, McDougall adopted an arrogant, impudent manner in his day-to-day dealings with his employees and business associates. He became a man who was despised in many quarters.

McDougall was oblivious to it all, however, and now took great pride in his appearance. When he strolled jauntily through the city streets it was rarely without an attractive female on his arm.

Towards the end of 1819, there was less of a swagger in McDougall's gait. His free-spending lifestyle, the spiralling cost of the mansion, and a particularly bad investment at the beginning of that year had bitten deeply into his capital. He was far from being in immediate financial trouble — his investments were still plentiful and profitable — but the sudden drain on his available cash did present obvious problems as well as shake his confidence.

It was almost certainly around this time that McDougall first gave prolonged and serious thought to a second major maritime fraud. He must have at some time before considered such a possibility, for on each occasion he had renewed the *Mary's* insurance, it was for the same excessive sum.

When McDougall eventually decided to make one more attempt to defraud the insurance companies he was influenced no doubt by the ease and problem-free aftermath of the 1816 exercise. Since the *Mary* was the obvious vessel to use in the crime, McDougall once again told James Menzies of his plans. The two men planned and prepared their strategy in the same manner as they had for the *Friends,* only on this occasion the candidate for the role of Master was much more obvious and readily available.

Languishing forlornly in the city jail was a middle-aged seaman named Archie McLachlan, held there following the successful prosecution by John McDougall to whom he owed a sum of money. McLachlan had borrowed the money — thought to be around £500 — two years previously in order to start up his own business. The venture had collapsed in less than 18 months and McLachlan had no means to repay his debts. McDougall

He visits McLachlan in Jail

had him thrown in jail. Now, in March 1820, he could see a way to a financial settlement that would be agreeable to both parties. He visited McLachlan and put to him the same proposition that had been offered to Robert Duncan four years earlier. The incentive for the seaman to accept the offer was McDougall's promise to withdraw his prosecution which meant his immediate release, plus the sum of £100 when the insurance was settled.

McDougall was stunned, angry and disappointed when his offer was rejected. He was determined, however, to press on with his plans and immediately placed newspaper advertisements to notify traders that the *Mary* would be sailing in May for Gibralter and Leghorn. It's not certain if any other seaman was offered the job as Master, but none was registered by mid-May when McLachlan summoned McDougall to the city jail and informed him that he had changed his mind. If the post of Master of the *Mary* was still available, he would now like to accept it. At almost the same time, James Menzies had contacted another money-hungry mariner and signed him on as First Mate. Now all was ready.

With a full cargo on board, the *Mary* sailed out of Glasgow at the end of May, 1820, and as McDougall and Menzies watched from the Broomielaw and waved goodbye, they felt satisfied that every preparation and precaution in their fraudulent scheme had been observed.

First stop for the *Mary* was Port Glasgow where part of the cargo was unloaded. She was there only a matter of hours before sailing to Port Bannatyne on Bute where the remainder of the goods were taken off. If everything went according to plan, the cargo on the island would later be re-shipped to England and the continent. The goods in Port Glasgow were loaded onto wagons, and taken back to Glasgow where, under cover of darkness, they were stored in a warehouse at Turner's Court.

Meantime, the fate of the *Mary* had been settled. Once back on her official route to Gibraltar, and about 40 miles off the Irish coast, Archie McLachlan went below to carry out the critical part of his agreement. He drilled six holes in the sloop's bottom then ran up on deck to inform the crew that the vessel had sprung a leak. He ordered everyone into the long boat, and two hours later, before being picked up by a Dutch schooner, they watched the dark bulk of the *Mary* disappear beneath the choppy surface of the Irish sea.

On their return to Glasgow, McLachlan informed McDougall that everything had gone smoothly and exactly as planned. The news elated McDougall who immediately lodged his claim for compensation with the insurance companies, then, with a crestfallen air, set about informing merchants that their goods were lying at the bottom of the Irish sea. As in the case of the *Friends,* an investigation by insurance agents was mounted and, as before, after questioning owners and crew members they could find no reason why payment should not be made.

Wasting no time, McDougall organised the sale of the goods taken off at Port Glasgow and now lying in his warehouse. When that was profitably concluded, he just as speedily dispersed the cargo that was unloaded at Port Bannatyne. It seemed another successful venture could be credited to the avaricious McDougall, but, by an amazing coincidence, things were soon to go horribly wrong.

Strolling at a sedate pace through the city streets on a warm July morning, about six weeks later, Colin Gillespie, one of Scotland's most respected calico printers, stopped for a few minutes at the Candleriggs to catch his breath. The elderly man paused near an archway under which sat a rather sickly-looking old woman with a basket at her side. She was one of the many city pedlars, who offered their wares to passers-by, half-begging, half-selling. Gillespie put his hand in his pocket and pulled out a sixpence. Before continuing up to Argyle Street, he handed the coin to her, politely refusing whatever piece of bric-a-brac she was extending.

"God bless you, sir", she said gratefully.

As he turned to go, his eye caught some of the contents of the woman's basket. She looked up at him and followed his puzzled gaze.

"Yes, sir?" she queried submissively. "Pick what you like, sir", she said, pushing the basket forward.

"Let me have a look at that cloth", said Gillespie, his voice sterner.

"Of course, sir, pick what you like, sir", she repeated nervously. From her basket she extracted a bundle of cloth made up of a dozen strips of various lengths. The old man took them and examined them carefully, his expression colder by the second. He knew by the texture and specific dye-colouring of the material that they were from his factory. But how did they come to be in the woman's basket when they were part of a three-bale batch shipped to Gibraltar aboard the sloop *Mary*, now at the bottom of the sea?

As he pondered on this, he was greeted by a close friend, James Dalglish, well-known in the clothing business.

"Look at this", Gillespie said, handing him one of the cloth remnants and explaining the situation.

The old lady became agitated. "Sir, I came by the cloth in an honest manner. I'm not a thief nor a resetter".

"Where did you buy them?" Dalglish asked firmly.

"It was not only me, sir. Seven or eight of us went up to John McDougall's warehouse in Turner's Court and he sold us the cloth very cheap".

Gillespie took a note of the woman's name and address then handed her another coin.

"I'm taking these remnants with me", he told her.

Before confronting McDougall, Gillespie, certain that the appearance of his material in the streets of Glasgow could not be innocently explained, decided to consult Charles Stewart, the Procurator Fiscal. The two men went to his office and told him what they'd discovered.

The *Mary's* fate did not have to be disclosed to Stewart, for it was common knowledge at the time. What did cause the Fiscal to look up from his desk was the disclosure by Gillespie that Archie McLachlan was the Master of the vessel. Just two days earlier, McLachlan had been arrested following a drunken brawl in which he stabbed and seriously injured another seaman named Morrison, and was now in jail awaiting trial. Stewart was also reminded of the transcation between the assailant and John McDougall a few months earlier. It seemed there was a definite reason for investigating the matter further.

Before meeting with McDougall, Stewart and Gillespie went straight to the city jail to question McLachlan. The Fiscal showed him the cloth and asked him to explain how, if the *Mary* went down on the way to Gibraltar, part of the cargo was being sold in the streets of Glasgow. The prisoner, already in a depressed state, became clearly distressed at this sudden and unexpected confrontation. He replied "I don't know", in the most resigned manner to almost every question put to him, and eventually dropped his head on to his hands and remained silent for many minutes.

Stewart exerted more pressure in an attempt to bluff his prisoner into an admission of some sort.

"I've already located several items that were supposed to have been lost, and the owners have identified them", he told McLachlan. "I know for certain that the cargo was abstracted and, from the statements I've taken from the other crew members, there is good reason to believe that the *Mary* was scutled. Since you were the Master what I want to know now is the full extent of your involvement. Do I have to inform you that this is a capital offence?"

That was all the persuasion McLachlan needed. The serious assault charge that already hung over him plus whatever charges would arise from the *Mary* incident were more than enough for the haggard mariner without the additional burden of protecting McDougall. It was with a degree of relish and no little interest that Stewart listened to the outpourings of Archie McLachlan.

Half an hour later, the Fiscal had all the information he required to arrest John McDougall, and, as he'd learned to his surprise, James Menzies. He summoned to his office his two chief messengers-at-arms, the brothers Alex and Stuart Turner, and two constables to accompany him to McDougall's office in St Enoch Square. Staff there informed him that McDougall was at his warehouse in Turner's Court, and when the officers arrived there they found him at his desk in one of the inner offices.

McDougall's reaction, on being informed that he was being arrested for fraud, was at first one of shock and disbelief, but as the minutes passed and the terrible reality dawned, his demeanour was reduced to hysteria. It would have been difficult for any of his associates, knowing him as a strong-willed and impudent giant of a man, to imagine him as he was now, submissive, cowardly, and begging for another chance. The Fiscal then instructed the two constables to go immediately to the Stockwell Street home of James Menzies and arrest him. He then began to interrogate McDougall.

In a very short period, John McDougall was in a state of virtual collapse. He blamed Menzies for his involvement, claiming that he had wanted nothing to do with the sinking of the ships, but it was only because of his partner's insistence that he had finally relented. ·

"Ships?" the Fiscal asked quietly, anxious not to alert him of his ignorance of the full extent of the crimes.

"The *Mary* was not the only one Menzies wanted sunk", blurted out McDougall. "He was in bad money trouble and desperately needed the insurance".

Without pressing, Stewart waited for him to continue, but McDougall lapsed into bouts of sobbing. Eventually, when he had regained a degree of self-control and realised his declaration of obvious contrition was receiving little sympathy, he offered the officers money to let him go. He had £1400 in ready cash in his safe which he wanted to give them with the promise of much more later. The offer was refused. He was allowed one concession, however: before being taken to jail he was escorted to the Turner brothers' house where he was locked in a security room until he had sorted out his personal affairs. In return for this favour, McDougall made a full and detailed confession of his part in the crimes. Shortly afterwards, he heard that James Menzies had escaped from custody.

Menzies had been arrested at his home and was being escorted to the city jail when he had broken free. It says a lot for the coolness of the man that he immediately made for the Thistle Bank and drew out £1200 from his account.

By October 1820, McDougall was imprisoned in the city jail at the Saltmarket wallowing in the deepest depression. He had been notified that he and Menzies (still at large) were being charged with: "Having in the month of June, 1816, feloniously sunk and destroyed, after having abstracted the cargo, the vessel called 'The Brigantine *Friends* of Glasgow', by means of boring holes in the bottom of the vessel and that for the purpose of defrauding and prejudicing the underwriters and owners of vessel and goods".

Under Statute law these crimes carried with them the death penalty.

McDougall's position appeared to be totally without hope. His verbal and written confession was obviously the strongest card in the Prosecutor's hand, and pleading "not guilty" now seemed a pointless exercise. Unless ... unless there was a way to discredit that confession.

Either by his own devices or at the suggestion of his legal advisers, McDougall concluded with some logic that the only way to reduce the impact that his confession would undoubtedly have on a trial jury was to persuade them that he was not in his right mind at the time he admitted his guilt.

With morale raised by this latest ploy, he set out to impress upon the prison authorities and doctors that he was mentally unstable. He began by lying naked on the floor of his cell absolutely motionless for hours on end, then suddenly bursting into fits of laughter for no apparent reason.

Whenever he was spoken to by any of the jailers, he would stare at them wide-eyed in the most intense way. At night he shrieked and howled like a wounded animal, evoking the curses and threats of other prisoners. Indeed, it got so bad that Thomas Young, the city hangman who resided at the jail, was forced to move out in order to get a night's sleep.

The limit for prison officials was reached when McDougall attacked a prison guard, leaping at him from all fours and biting him on the leg. At the end of November, the prisoner was committed to the city lunatic asylum and remained there for observation and treatment until December 8 when he was returned to jail. From then until his trial, he was kept in a special cell away from the other prisoners.

His trial began in May 1821, at the High Court of Admiralty in Edinburgh, by which time he had become more reasonable and subdued. As expected, the first major issue to arise was on the opening day when the Crown attempted to introduce the accused's confession. John (later Lord) Murray for the defence questioned its admissability on the grounds that it was penned and uttered by a man who was of unsound mind. Thus, on the 5th May, began a two-day pre-trial to determine the balance of McDougall's mind at that period and consequently the validity of his confession.

First witness for the defence was William Durie, Superintendent of the lunatic asylum, who testified that the prisoner was "exceedingly restless and distracted" during his time at the asylum, "and did not continue a moment in the same place". Next to be called were Walter Morrison and John Rutherford who were employed by Glasgow Magistrates to attend the prisoner to ensure he did no harm to himself. They related that in the six-week period they attended McDougall he looked and acted like a man deranged. He had lucid moments, they claimed, but for the most part he behaved in the most idiotic manner.

The defence called four physicians from different parts of the city and each in turn testified that they had examined the accused and and studied his behaviour while in jail. They were all of the opinion that his mind was disturbed to the extent that he should be in a lunatic asylum.

The Crown also called four doctors, and their testimony was as damning as the defence's was extenuating. Three of them were of the opinion, based on hours of observation and questioning, that the prisoner was faking his insanity. The fourth drew his conclusions from what was considered a more practical experiment at that time. Dr James Corkindale decided to test the genuineness of McDougall's symptoms by strapping him into a mechanical contraption called a whirley-gig. The device was delivered to the courtyard of the jail after Dr Corkindale saw children playing on it at a carnival on nearby Glasgow Green. The prisoner was taken from his cell and strapped into the seat positioned at the end on a metal arm extending from the centre of the device. One of the guards proceeded to turn a handle and the seat began to turn.

"Faster", ordered the doctor, and the guard duly obliged. The device built up speed until those observing became quite concerned about the safety of the equipment.

"For God's sake, Doctor. Stop, please", cried McDougall, his face sickly white. "My head's spinning. I'm going to be sick".

The doctor called to the guard to stop and when the contraption came to rest he took McDougall's pulse and examined his mouth and eyes. From those brief tests he adjudged that the prisoner "exhibited not real but counterfeited symptoms of insanity". The basis of his conclusion being that an insane person would not have the intelligence to know fear.

At the end of the two-day hearing, during which time the weight of evidence was very much against the defence, the Judge Admiral, Sir John Connell, adjudged that McDougall was of sound mind when he made his confession and feigned insanity afterwards in an attempt to devalue it. He therefore ruled against the objection and allowed the statement to be read.

The look of abject misery on the face of the accused reflected his trial prospects. He knew he was a doomed man.

John Murray, leading a four-man defence team, was one of the most gifted and respected lawyers in Glasgow. That his client would be found guilty was never in doubt, but all his efforts and ingenuity were now directed to saving him from the gallows. He gambled on making one last desperate effort to save McDougall's life.

On the eve of the last day of the trial he stumbled upon one, almost insignificant detail which he dismissed at first, but came back to time and again until he realised it was virtually all there was left — the last round in the chamber. He used the exact wording of the clause of the statute law under which his client was charged to base his final plea. It read:-

"That if any owner of, or captain, master, officer, or mariner, belonging to, any ship or vessel, shall, after the first day of September, in the year 1789, willfully cast away, burn, or otherwise destroy, the ship or vessel of which he is the owner, or to which he belongeth, or in anywise direct or procure the same to be done ... shall suffer death, as in other cases of capital crime".

During his summing up on the last day, 11th May 1821, Murray drew the jury's attention to the word "owner".

"The first and main question for you to consider", he told them, "is whether or not you find yourselves authorised to convict the panel on the statute on which the charge is founded. It is evident that unless he comes under the description of an owner, the statute can by no means apply to him. Can any person who has only one third interest in a property be classified as the owner?"

Murray spoke forcibly and eloquently for 45 minutes, much of the time urging the jury members that they must judge by and comply with the letter of the law, but also part of the time endeavouring to divert the bulk of his client's guilt on to the shoulders of the outlawed James Menzies. During all this time, in fact almost the entire last day, McDougall sat hunched forward in his seat, staring at the floor. At 2 pm the Judge Admiral summed up, touching on most significant parts of the evidence and any that was controversial. Not at any time during his speech did he extend or encourage one glimmer of hope for the prospects or future of the distraught prisoner.

Before the jury retired at 2.30pm he instructed them that if they should bring in a verdict against the prisoner — that is, anything other than an acquittal — they should make it a special one and should stipulate into which category his guilt fell — statute law or common law, the latter being non-capital.

It was 24 hours later when the jury returned with their verdict. When the prisoner was asked to stand prior to it being announced, he did so with an ashen face and a great deal of weariness. He stood upright, his expression sad, shoulders stooped, staring straight ahead, not daring to look in the direction of the jury. When he heard the announcement — "We find the accused guilty at common law", he fell forward in a dead faint.

The decision of the jury hardly pleased the Judge Admiral. He made it clear before pronouncing sentence that he could not find one single alleviating factor in McDougall's circumstances. Had the jury found him guilty by statute he would have had no alternative but to sentence him to death. As it was, the sentence pronounced was that of "perpetual infamy and transportation for life". That the overjoyed, triumphant John McDougall escaped the hangman's noose infuriated the staid, thrice-weekly *Glasgow Courier,* whose editorial pontificated:

"A system of more complicated and deliberate villainy has rarely, if ever, been brought before our criminal courts. Had the jury found him guilty under the statute law, the sentence must have been death. But it seems they had some doubts if a person only 'part owner' of a vessel could come within the strict meaning of the words 'owner of' in the Act. The jury gave the prisoner the benefit of the doubt. What has taken place, however, on this occasion, the deep and deliberate system of fraud, perjury, robbery and injustice displayed, and yet the perpetrator has escaped the capital punishment which these heinous crimes merited, will, we trust, show the legislature the necessity of making the law more clear and explicit, so that, in future, no such doubts may occur".

McDougall and Menzies were also charged with the sinking of the *Mary* and their trial set for late May, but this was suspended following McDougall's sentence, and with Menzies still at large. In August 1821, McDougall was transported to Botany Bay for the rest of his life.

There was one ironic postscript left to relate in this unique case concerning his partner, James Menzies. Whereas McDougall feigned insanity in his attempt to escape justice, and failed, Menzies feigned partial blindness and succeeded. The latter wandered the county of Fife masquerading as a beggar blind in his left eye. For the purpose of realism, he used a solution of some kind to keep his eyelids shut, then covered the eye with a dirty piece of cloth. Since he was constantly on the move, he occasionally made the right eye "blind". Eventually his sight was affected by whatever oint-

ment or paste he was using, and by the time he was in his late fifties he was
sightless. One way or another, justice was served on the two men who were
involved in one of Scotland's most unusual cases.

The Scottish Empress
of Morocco

BY A.C.McKERRACHER

Many Scots have risen from lowly beginnings to high office through
dedication and hard work. This is the story of a country girl from Perthshire who attained one of the most exalted ranks of all — Empress of
Morocco — through no effort or even desire on her part.

She was Helen Gloag, born in January, 1750, at Wester Pett near
Muthill, the daughter of Andrew Gloag and Ann Key. In that year, the
surrounding district lay subdued and poverty-stricken for its principal lan-
downer, the Earl of Perth, had been attainded for his part in the '45
Jacobite Uprising, and his Drummond Castle estate had been forfeited to
the Crown. As the Episcopal religion was still banned, Helen Gloag was
baptised secretly in St James's Church, Muthill, on 14th February, 1750.

Some time later, her family moved a short distance to the Mill of Steps
on the Machany Water where her father was in business as a blacksmith.

This little hamlet consisted then of a waulk mill, a smithy, and a square of cottages beside a small stone bridge which carried the recently-built Stirling to Crieff military road over the river.

Helen grew up to be a striking beauty, with green eyes, golden red hair and high cheekbones set in a pale, oval face. Her mother died when she was quite young, and her father re-married, but unfortunately, the new Mrs Gloag and her growing stepdaughter did not get on together. Matters became worse when Helen was in her teens, for she began a friendship with a local farmer, John Byrne, who was 11 years her senior. She made frequent visits to his nearby farm of Lurg to play cards, and although it was a quite innocent relationship, it became the source of ever-increasing friction with her stepmother.

When Helen was 19, she decided she could stand it no longer, and she resolved to emigrate to South Carolina in America along with several of her girl friends. The little party made its way to Greenwich in May, 1769, and took passage on a ship which they hoped would carry them to a new and better life.

The vessel had been at sea for only a few weeks when from the masthead came the dreaded cry, "Corsairs!" — and bearing in fast on all sides came a pack of the feared Xebecs. These swift, three-masted ships of 200 tons carried 20 guns and 200 of the terrible Salle pirates. The scourge of the seas, these men had their base at the Moroccan port of Salle where a sand bar at the harbour mouth allowed the nimble xebecs to sail across to safety leaving any larger pursuer floundering impotently outside.

Salle, an ancient walled town, had become notorious for its school of pilots and piracy, founded originally by Moors driven from Spain. Its graduates roamed the seas as far north as Orkney seeking booty and slaves. In 1631, they had raided a village in the west of Ireland, and carried off 250 people. Raids by the pirates were common right around the British coast.

Some of the pirates were renegades — captured Europeans who had spurned Christianity to escape slavery, and had sworn allegiance to the Sultan of Morocco and embraced Mohammedanism. Many Scots were amongst them, including one Robert Carr who changed his name to Omar, and was given command of a 16-gun xebec in 1757. The Sultan of Morocco owned over half the pirate fleet, and collected a tax of 60% on all captured goods.

The defenceless merchant ship which carrried Helen and her friends was no match for the well-armed pirate vessels, and the savage corsairs swarmed aboard cutting down all who resisted. The male survivors were chained and sent into the galleys as slaves, while the women were herded into the hold under guard. The triumphant pirates made their way back to Salle with their prize, and as the terrified women were brought up on deck they gazed in horror at scenes of utter barbarism, for around Salle's walls were fixed human heads (this custom was last recorded in 1912 when 40 rebel heads adorned the walls of Fez, and the Salle pirates were not finally stamped out until 1921).

The country the girls were entering was a living hell for captured Europeans, as Moroccans regarded Christians as sub-human, and of less worth than animals. However, by 1769, conditions had improved somewhat since the reign of the terrible Mulai (Prince) Ismail, who had ruled Morocco with a bloodstained iron fist from 1672 to 1727. Mulai Ismail was of part Negro descent, and delighted in matching the fairest of his captives with the blackest of his Negro bodyguard.

During his reign, over 25,000 Christian slaves were employed in huge construction works, particularly the Palace at Meknes whose stables alone stretch for three miles, and were designed to hold 12,000 horses. The slaves were kept at night in underground dungeons, and treated with the utmost cruelty. During his tours of inspection, Mulai Ismail would suddenly order a slave to be flung alive into a lime kiln, or impaled on a stake, while his favourite delight was to saw a man in half from the head down. His cruelty extended to his own people, and he would lop off an attendant's head to test the sharpness of his sword.

He had a harem of 2000 women, each of whom he visited only once, and had 1000 children of whom only 520 sons survived, for he had his daughters strangled at birth. It is said that on one occasion, he desired that a captive 15-year old English girl should become his wife, and he had her feet plunged repeatedly into boiling oil until she converted to Moham-medanism.

There was great concern in Britain over the plight of Christian slaves in Morocco, and the records of many Scots kirk sessions contain entries like: "To a seaman with his tongue cut out by the Moors, 2/10d". Many wealthy merchants endowed property whose rent was used to ransom slaves, and this, rather than the version given in history books, is possibly the real reason behind the famous house in Edinburgh's Canongate called Morocco Land, with its stone effigy of a moor.

Helen and her friends were shipped ashore to be spat at and reviled by the onlookers. The men were led away in chains to an unimaginable living death, while the less attractive women were taken out and given to the Moorish soldiers for their amusement. Those of better looks, including Helen, were dragged to the slave market to be exhibited for sale. Here, Helen's beauty attracted the attention of an astute merchant who paid a large sum for her and then presented her to the Grand Vizier as a gift for Sultan Sidi Mohammed ibn Abdullah, the ruler of Morocco.

He had inherited the throne in 1757, and was more enlightened than his fearful grandfather although he still encouraged slavery and piracy. He quickly became infatuated by his new concubine, and shortly after, he made Helen his fourth wife and raised her to the rank of Empress. This must have been not long after Helen arrived, for in 1769 an Englishwoman called Mrs Crisp was captured while travelling to Minorca, and taken into the Sultan's harem. Inexplicably, she was freed unharmed soon after, and wrote a book about her adventures, *The Female Captive*. In it she recorded that she had heard of the Sultan having an "Irish" wife and wondered if it was because of her that she had been released.

Unfortunately, Morocco was a closed country for centuries, and the very few native records that were written would not consider mentioning anything so unimportant as a woman — even if she was an Empress. However, there are one or two fragments to be gleaned from the writings of the few Europeans who were allowed to enter the country. Perhaps it was due to Helen's influence that an English doctor, William Lemprière, was allowed into Morocco in 1789, and even permitted to examine the ladies in the harem. He wrote later that while he had met three of the royal wives, the fourth was in the town of Fez, but rumour had it she was English. This seems to fit, for Helen would then have been 39, and after 30, a Sultana was usually sent into exile with her children.

There seems little doubt that Helen did exert a strong influence over her husband, for later in his reign the shipping of negro slaves from Morocco (by the English!) was forbidden. British captives were released unharmed, slavery dwindled away, and even the Salle pirates were officially abolished. Most interestingly, trade compacts and treaties were entered into with the British, and in 1782, aid was given to them in their battle for Gibraltar. Thus it seems more than likely that it was due partly to Helen Gloag that Gibraltar is British today.

The Sultam Mohammed began to build towns for trading purposes, and his new Atlantic port of Mogador (now Essaouira) attracted traders from all over Europe. Here came vast camel caravans from the interior, laden with ivory, gold, carpets and wax. The port of Mogador was originally named after its patron saint Sidi Magdoul, whose shrine still stands. Believe it or not, Sidi Magdoul is said to have been a Scots seaman called John MacDougall, but when he was there, and what made him a Muslim saint is uknown.

Helen had two sons by the Sultan, and seems to have become reconciled to her strange life in a barbarous land. She wrote home frequently, and sent many gifts of Moroccan craftsmanship not only to her family, but also to her friend John Byrne. These were conveyed by Robert Gloag, Helen's sea captain brother who made many trips to see her, and it is likely he was one of several Scots who were permitted to establish trading houses.

In 1790, Sultan Mohammed ibn Abdullah died and as Helen's sons were too young to rule, he had nominated a newphew to succeed him. Unfortunately, his disowned son by a German concubine, the half-mad, red-haired Mulai Yazeed, raised a revolt and grabbed his father's throne. The first act of the sadistic Yazeed was to roast alive his father's faithful Vizier, and then to throw his harem into the streets. After the Basha of Tangier held out against him, Yazeed ordered the man's aged mother to be put to death in a horrific manner. The details of his mindless cruelty are not fit for these pages.

To escape Yazeed's reign of terror, Helen sent her sons, then aged about 21 and 16, to the town of Teuten, where they sought sanctuary in one of the few newly-permitted Christian monasteries. She then appealed

Invasion of the Pirates!

for help to the British Government, claiming her British citizenship, and a fleet prepared to sail to her assistance from Gibraltar. An officer, Lt Colonel Jardine, was sent ahead to ascertain the situation, but before he arrived, Yazeed's troops probably overran the monastery and murdered the two princes. Politics being what they are, the fleet sent to help Helen was then directed to aid the usurper Yazeed in his bid to throw the Spanish out of the Moroccan town of Cueta. For the next two years, Morocco once again became a living nightmare until Yazeed died of a wound in 1792.

Unfortunately, Helen's fate is unknown, but it is possible that she survived Yazeed's reign. Some years ago, two ladies from Muthill were visiting the modern town of Rabat built on the other bank of the river from the old pirate town of Salle, and now the Moroccan capital, when their guide suddenly pointed out a monument which he said had been erected to the memory of a Scottish Empress. Morocco still seems to be something of a closed country for despite many enquiries, I have been unable to track down the memorial's location.

Helen's sea captain brother retired to the old family cottage at Mill of Steps and died there in 1830 aged 77. Many of her letters and gifts were in the possession of a Mrs McCall, granddaughter of the farmer John Byrne, until her death in 1922 aged 83. Mrs McCall also owned the chair in which Helen had sat to play cards at Lurg farm when she was a teenager, and this was rescued from a rubbish pile after a disposal sale. It was known as the Empress Chair, but unfortunately only a few woodworm-eaten parts survive today in Muthill.

This is not the only reminder of Helen Gloag for in Muthill today lives a descendant of her sea captain brother. This lady with her auburn hair and green eyes must closely resemble the simple country girl who became the Scottish Empress of Morocco, and entranced a Sultan with her beauty.

Lodging for eleven 'Witches'

BY DOROTHY K HAYNES

In the year 1649, the Marquis of Douglas had eleven women rounded up and locked in the Lanark Tolbooth, accused of witchcraft. The Town Council are said to have been very much disturbed and displeased. An expert pricker, George Cathie, was called in to examine the "witches", but, despite his conscientious efforts, he found no witches' spots on them and, at their trial, all were acquitted and set free.

This information is from *Lanark: the Burgh and its Councils, 1469-1880,* by A D Robertson.

The gaol was on the shady side of the High Street, but it got the sun in the early morning. Yellow light shone through the criss-cross bars to the rough stone inside, and Sam Skinner dozed at the top of the steps, making the most of the warmth.

"Sam!" roared the Provost, raised from his bed by an early messenger. "Get off that chair and get busy! There's eleven witches coming this morning and — "

"Witches? *Weemen* witches?"

"Yes. You'll have to shuffle the men round a bit. Get the place redd up. I'm going home for my breakfast".

The gaoler stared after him, swinging his keys and looking harassed. He had never met a witch. He knew that some towns were bedevilled with them, and that some gaolers had the bother of burning them, a job he didn't fancy at all. Sighing, he went off to chivvy the men around so that the best cell, the one facing the street, could be refurbished for the ladies.

When the Provost came back, pernickety and resentful, Sam tried to get to the bottom of the matter. It was his gaol, and he was entitled to know about the occupants.

"Why do we have to have them, Provost? We've enough work in Lanark with our ain criminals — "

"Oh, it's the higher-ups Sam, the higher-ups". He glossed over the niceties of the inter-burgh feud in which he had been temporarily bested. "But I tell you this, Sam, you're going to have your work cut out. Witches are chancy creatures".

It was late afternoon when the witches arrived. They stood with their wrists bound behind them, lurching and stumbling as the cart came down the High Street, and the Provost scowled nervously as the carter let down the tailboard and hustled them on their way.

"I wish you luck o' them", he grumbled. "Twenty years I've made this journey, and I've never had a load like yon. Burnin's too good for them ..."

"They're not going to be ... burned, are they?" asked Sam nervously.

"Certainly not", snapped the Provost. "They've not even been tried yet. Though by the look of them", he added sourly, "they're up to all the devilment of the day".

He watched as the women were chased up the steps by the reluctant

Sam. He checked them off on his fingers, nine, ten, hard-faced hussies all of them. Was there one short? There would be hell to pay if one of them had escaped — but no. Here was the eleventh, her head low, her hair covering her face, the only one of the eleven to look ashamed.

"Are you ... one of those?" he asked dubiously.

Her voice was so low that he had to bend to hear it. "So they tell me, sir".

"What's your name?"

"Gillian, sir. Gillian Watson".

"Hrmm". He turned to consult with Sam, but Sam was inside, battling volubly with his charges. Thoughtfully, the Provost walked away.

It was the beginning of a nightmare for Sam Skinner. Left to himself, he would have let the lot go, and good riddance. He was an easy-going fellow and he and the regulars understood each other. A young prisoner was more amenable by day if he could spend the odd night with his wife, and if a father went out after dark to poach for his children, Sam's pot was filled at the same time.

But now security was tighter. The Provost kept a daily check on the prisoners, because the witches, though housed in his gaol, belonged to another burgh, which would hold him responsible if anything went wrong.

Luckily, they were in reasonable spirits. Their cell had a view of sorts. They could hear the burn in the High Street when the rain was heavy, and there was always someone willing to stand at the window and talk, even if all they did was to shout insults.

In this matter the witches were more than able to look after themselves. They would hold on to the bars and yell, especially at the men. They stirred up the other prisoners, so that there was a constant coarse exchange from cell to cell, wild laughter, bawdy songs. "Oh, Provost, you'll have to do something!" moaned Sam. "This gaol was such a quiet, couthie place!".

"You're right", said the Provost. "Enough's enough. I'll tell you what we'll do. I'll take it on myself. We'll prove them. Mind you", he added regretfully, "pricking costs public money; but, then, so does food".

●　　●　　●　　●　　●　　●

The pricker arrived, a pale man with a black box and a black hat over his eyes and, as the rumour went round, the witches milled around in their cell like hens disturbed by a fox. While the platform was being built at the Cross, he dined with the Provost and elaborated on his art.

"They've all got a blind spot, you know, a dead spot that canna feel pain. What we do is cover their eyes and go over them with a needle. They squeal all right when the point goes in, I guarantee that". He wiped his lips and laughed dourly. "But when I get to the dead spot. they don't even know I've touched them".

"Whereabouts is the spot?"

"Anywhere. Sometimes they dinna ken themselves. But I find it. Eleven, you said?"

"Aye, eleven", said the Provost, after a pause.

● ★ ★ ★ ★ ★

The women were led out, tied, a halter round their necks. They were stripped before the crowd, and where people might have felt pity, it turned to disgust at the way the objects behaved, giggling, with their eyes bound, as the pricker felt them over. Every time the needle bit, they screamed and shouted indecencies, but one after another they were acquitted. There was no dead spot. They cavorted rudely on the platform after their acquittal; and then it was the turn of the young one, Gillian, standing quivering and silent, having seen and heard all that was to happen to her.

The Provost, long sickened, could hardly look as she stood, afraid of the long needles, and yet afraid not to feel them. He winced at every stab, at every little cry she gave; and then the man in black lost patience and pushed her aside. They were wasting his time, he said. There wasn't a witch among them. He wiped his weapons on his sleeve, took his money and rode off disgruntled. He was paid extra for convictions.

"So what do we do now, Provost?" asked Sam, eager to get the place back to normal. "Turn them all loose again?"

"Aye. Tell them they'll be whipped if they're not gone within the hour".

So Sam prepared to harry them out. Surprisingly, they were loth to go. After their brazen show on the platform, first one and then another had broken down in the pain of their smarting skins and then the spunk went out of the lot of them, so that Sam had to harden his heart towards them. He drove them out like cattle, and then went back to take out the foul straw and get the regulars back to their quarters.

At first he thought it was a rat rustling in the corner, but as he peered, his rake lifted, he saw it was the girl Gillian.

"D'you no ken you're free?" he said, clearing the floor energetically. "The others are all away by this". He came closer, bending to peer into her face. "Are you feared for me?" he asked, almost gently.

She shook her head. "I dinnae want to go with *them*", she whispered. "They're coorse".

"Well, you cannae stay here. The men will be back".

She got to her feet at that and stood happing her shawl around her; and at that moment the Provost came to see that all was in order.

Sam quickly unloaded the problem on to him. "... and she's a wee bit above the others, ye ken ..."

"Of course, of course". He bit his lip and swithered. "You don't know anyone needing a housekeeper, do you? I take it you can bake and clean and so on, my dear?"

She gave what looked like a curtsey.

"What aboot yersel, Provost? You were sayin' the other day — "

"That's different, different altogether".

Nevertheless it was a solution. The Provost had never married and his housekeeper was getting old and donnert. Gillian looked like a likely lass and, now that she had been cleared of the stigma of witchcraft, there was really no reason ... "Come away with me just now", he said. "Dear me, the worry and the bother ..."

Provost Hamilton sent the pricker's bill to the burgh which had sent the witches. The bill was promptly disclaimed, even when he pointed out that one of them, unjustly accused, was at present being employed at his own expense as housekeeper.

It was not, however, an entirely profitless transaction. The Provost's house shone, his porridge was smooth and hot, his kailpot always bubbling. As the weeks went by, Gillian was heard to sing at her work and seen to smile to herself. She had taken to walking out with Sam Skinner, who told everyone that she was a tidy wee thing and that it was about time he settled down.

The Provost eyed this growing romance with misgivings. Where Gillian had been wont to sit by the fire at night, her hands busy, her face calm and cheerful, she now spent evenings with Sam, while he, the one who had taken her in and helped her to respectability, had to pass the time alone. Council meetings grew boring, the tavern seemed dirty and noisome; and he could not settle until he heard the sound of irritatingly long farewells at the back door and the click of the latch as she came in, flushed and shy and radiant.

What could he do? He couldn't deny her freedom on her day off, and he dared not be harsh to her, lest he should hurt her feelings and give her cause to seek work elsewhere. It was Sam who was the villain, Sam who was spoiling everything. Dourly, the Provost paid a visit to the gaol, where Sam Skinner was sweeping the steps, sending brown dust rolling into the fresh morning.

"It's time you paid more attention to your business, Sam. That's about a month's dirt you're raising there. And while we're on the subject, you'll have to keep those charges of yours quiet at nights. I've had complaints about singing till two in the morning".

"Och, but Provost, we've aye turned a blind eye to a wee bit celebration — "

"Nothing of the sort. The Council makes the rules, Skinner, not you. You're getting above yourself these days".

"And what would you mean by *that*, Mr Hamilton?" Sam purposely dropped the title, and the Provost's lips tightened.

"Just what I say. I don't like the way you've been taking up with my housekeeper". He hesitated, looking for some way of saying it less harshly, but the only way was to come out with it plainly and to the point. "She's no ordinary girl for you to pick up, you know. She's got a position to think about now. She's my housekeeper, and it doesn't suit me to have the Provost's servant walking out with the town gaoler".

Sam's face was white as he gripped his broom.

"I think *she* might have opinions about that, Provost".

"No she hasn't. I've already explained the position, and she agrees with me".

It was a lie, but to Sam it seemed quite feasible. Provosts were a law unto themselves. He turned and went into the gaol, banging the heavy door, and the Provost, half ashamed, went home to ensure that, whatever else happened, his housekeeper would stay with him for life.

●   ●   ●   ●   ●

There was less talk than he expected. A few sniggers, perhaps, about the auld deevil getting a lass half his age, but in a way that was a compliment. The wedding was celebrated with dignified gaiety, and the Provost setled down in triumphant joy with his douce little wife.

When he found that they were to have a child, he felt that fortune had been almost too good to him. There she was, his plump little pet, sewing fine white clothes for the baby. Her needle flashed as it tracked along the seam, stab, stab, through the cloth — and into her finger; he watched the red dots marking the hem, and it was a little while before the joy drained out of him as the colour drained from his face. She had pricked her finger, deep into the flesh — *and she didn't feel a thing!*

A maist barberus Bangsterrie
BY ALEX R MITCHELL

It came as rather a jolt to me to learn that many of my Glaswegian ancestors were just as forthright, fond of a dram, violent and gallus as are some of today's inhabitants. This discovery came when I was examining some 17th century records of Glasgow's Kirk Session and minutes of the Town Council.

The Kirk of those days frowned on light entertainment. A dictum dated May 24, 1624, reads: "Intimation of resetting (presenting) Comedians, Jugglers, etc., is forbidden, such resetters to be punished".

But some entertainers were officially approved. In that same month a council minute reveals: "The pipers and drummers to be given as meikle red claith as will mak a coit, brekis and hoises".

The recipients of this bounty were directed to make the uniforms themselves. Some of the cloth was to be "maid up in jupe fassion", i.e., in the form of a kilt.

Unladylike behaviour was common enough in those early days in Glasgow. A fierce feud apparently existed between the Clogy and the Sauchie families. Miss Elspeth Clogy was found guilty of "the casting of stanes" at Miss Christiane Sauchie and biting a piece out of her arm.

Elspeth's mother and sister and Christiane's mother and father were all involved in the fracas. But only the fearsome Elspeth was found guilty and she was put in the stocks for a day and in jail for a month.

More domestic discord centred round the unfortunate Mrs Margaret Touris. Her husband, John, and a tailor, John Mure, appeared before the Provost and magistrates. Mure "cast ane stane" at Mrs Touris. Then, for some unknown reason, Mr Touris "cast stanes at his guidwife's pigs". Next, the unpredictable Mr Touris smote Mr Mure "to the effusion of his bluid". Touris and Mure were jailed for eight days.

The Kirk Session was a powerful body. On April 14, 1642, the members directed ministers and council officials to go through the streets on Sunday nights and apprehend "absentees from church, swearers, blasphemers and mockers of piety".

Absentees were publicly rebuked. Swearers were fined 12 pence, and piety-mockers were made to stand for long spells at the kirk door. A significant entry in the records reads: "Twa hair gownes for the use of the Kirk".

The Town Council members were an arrogant lot, too. On February 22, 1612, William Watson appeared before the Provost and magistrates accused of uttering "disdaynefull speiches to them with his bonet on his heid".

Mr Watson was quite unrepentant, and declared he would "neither acknowledge provost nor baillie nor king". He was thereupon fined £10, thrown into jail for a night, and ordered "to walk bair-heidit to the Cross and after being put in irons thair for fower oors to go on his knees and ask God's mercie and the baillies' pardon for his hie contempt". A raw deal for a man who spoke his mind.

A little later another honest Glasgow man disapproved of the non-elected corrupt council. This candid chap, Peter Adam, made his feelings clear to the City Treasurer. Adam made a particularly earthy crack against the civic dignitaries. The Treasurer reported him, and the shocked council fined their reckless critic "twentie pundis" and jailed him for eight days.

Violent assaults were, as now, not uncommon in 17th century Glasgow. On January 25, 1612, the Provost and magistrates found Richard Herbertson guilty of assault — described as "a maist barberus bangsterrie on James Watts, his son John and thair grit dog". The big dog was killed in what must have been quite a battle.

Herbertson was put in the stocks at Glasgow Cross for a day, and the body of the dog was laid beside him. From the stocks he was taken to face the magistrates again and ordered to pay the dog's owner £40. After that he was to spend a month in the town jail.

A charge of attacking "ane young damsell" was preferred against Matthew Thomson, described as "ane hieland fidler". The charge was found "hard to be verifiet", but there was no acquittal for the Highland fiddler. The magistrates decided that he was "ane idyll vagabond" and ordered his banishment from the city forever, with the warning, "If he be found within this toun hereafter he sall be hangit".

The magistrates made a strange bargain with one Malcolm McCallan when they found him guilty of "the hurting and bleeding of John Paterson". McCallan was sentenced to banishment from the city, "and if he be found in the toun thereafter he sall be nailed by the lug to the wall of the Tron Kirk". He was then told that the sentence would be quashed if he paid his victim £20.

A mysterious entry in the Kirk Session record is headed, "Smothering Children". The Presbytery decided that "Smoorers of children make their repentance two Sundays in sackcloth standing at the kirk door". Life was cheap, especially for children. One shudders at the thought of what the infant mortality rate must have been like in those days.

Another entry hints that there might have been an experimental avant garde theatre in Rutherglen in the middle of the 17th century. "The playing of bagpipes on a Sunday is forbidden", the Church leaders proclaim sternly. "And there will be no Bickering or Plays. Golf, bowls, etc., are forbidden on Sunday". Lastly, almost as an afterthought, the grim warning, "No person to go to Ruglen to see Vain Plays".

The Kirk Session came down very heavily on those found guilty of extra-marital love affairs. The minimum sentence was "only 8 days in The Steeple, one day on the stool of repentance and one day standing at the kirk door".

The call-girls of the day must have found the going tough. The pillars of the Kirk ordered "a cart to be made to cart Harlots through the toun and appoints a pulley to be made on the Bridge whereby adulterers may be ducked in the Clyde".

From the 300-year-old Kirk and Town Council records it is apparent that women in Glasgow at that time were regarded very much as second-rate citizens. The city's two midwives were ordered to obtain the permission of ministers or magistrates before attending pregnant unmarried

A Ducking in the Clyde

women. And the Kirk Session had strong complaints about women occupying church seats reserved for men. Wives had to stand or sit on the floor.

A petulant note creeps into the Kirk records when women are mentioned. "No woman will come within the kirk with her plaid above her head nor will she lie down upon the floor", states one entry. It goes on: "Great disorder hath been in the kirk by women having their heads covered in time of sermon".

Considering that many a sermon went on for over two hours, who, but those unco guid Kirk leaders, could blame housewives for snatching forty winks in the church?

The Town Council of 1610 was, as now, concerned at the city's high crime rate. Mugging was common. The record reveals: "There are manifold troublances committit by notorious tulzeors, fechters and nycht-walkers". Eight days in prison was the minimum sentence for a mugger. Women offenders were manacled and made to stand for long spells at Glasgow Cross.

But, of course, Kirk and civic authorities were not solely concerned with the moral welfare of the community. Some three centuries before Rangers and Celtic came into being — on Februaury 19,1609, to be exact — John Neill was commissioned by the council to supply "fute bolls" to the town.

An incomprehensible item is minuted in the same month with the heading: "Powder for the Town Youths". It goes on to disclose that the baillies had sanctioned the expenditure of £10 "for pouther to the young men of the toun for when the Duke of Wortinburg comes to the toun".

Four council officers were given £20 "for their expenxses in transporting 4 hielandmen to Lynlithgow". The captain of the escort was allowed £10 "for mending ane halberd damaged in followyng said hielandmen".

The council minute that intrigued me most is that of July 20, 1611. I like to think of the worthy Provost and baillies of Glasgow sitting in solemn conclave to consider "Tin chanties for the Castle". They decided to pay Marion Pollock "ane pund for twa tin watter pottis sent to the castle of the Erll of Dumbarris".

It makes one feel there's a certain glamour lacking in the deliberations of our district and regional councils.

Bridges and homes swept away in the Great Moray Floods

BY PATRICIA M. BINGHAM

What is happening to our weather? Has our mild, temperate climate become a thing of the past? in the winter of 1978, we had the severe Highland blizzards and over 1981/2, there was the "Big Freeze", with its record low temperatures. What few of us realise is that such extreme weather conditions have not been confined to recent years, and if we take a look back, we might think ourselves fortunate.

Over 200 years ago, the Moray Firth and its adjoining regions suffered disastrous conditions, which exceeded by far anything we have experienced this century.

Spates and flash floods were not unknown in the North-east and in 1768 and 1799 conditions were recorded as being severe. However, the events which took place between 12th July and 5th August in 1829 were terrifying enough to earn the title "The Great Moray Floods".

The months of May, June and July of that year had been unusually humid and dry, and local farmers were becoming concerned for their ripening crops. Understandably so, as agriculture was the main source of income, employment and export in the area. Widespread drought occurred, endangering livestock and crops alike, and although the days of unbearable heat were occasionally interrupted by spells of heavy rain and strong winds, they were short-lived and the situation remained largely unaltered.

Weird, frightening sights were reported. Several large waterspouts were seen whirling across fields, uprooting and carrying everything in their paths. The aurora borealis was unusually vivid in colour, especially in July, and during the day the sky was often tinged with a bronze hue, filling everyone with apprehension. As the hot days went by, the tension continued to climb.

On Sunday 12th July, during a heavy rainstorm, the innkeeper in a Ross-shire village took shelter beneath the arch of a bridge. The bed of the burn had almost completely dried up because of the drought, but suddenly he saw a huge wall of water rushing towards him, carrying with it soil, uprooted trees and large stones. For a moment he just stared, then ran for his life. The great mass was halted briefly by the bridge, then it tore through, taking the stonework with it, and roared onwards to flood the plains of the loch below.

When the local folk returned from church, and found the bridge swept away, they could only stand horrified and watch as their homes were destroyed and crops and topsoil disppeared before their eyes. They were convinced that only their village had been struck, by the hand of God, because of their landlord's recent vote in Parliament for Roman Catholic emancipation! Unknown to them, their disaster was but the first in a sequence of catastrophic events.

Three weeks later, on Saturday 1st August, what looked like a huge black cloud was seen travelling across the Moray Firth in a southward direction. It proved to be a vast waterspout soaring skywards, lifting everything in its path until it finally broke over the Monadhliaths at Kingussie early the following morning.

The Rivers Findhorn and Nairn, and their tributaries, became swollen, raging torrents. Heavy rain began and continued for the next three days. High winds drove the deluge so that no window succeeded in keeping it out. Swollen rivers boomed like distant cannon, and those trees which were still standing were stripped naked of their leaves. Landmarks and buildings throughout the countryside were obliterated, and even small animals, birds and game were killed by the force of the downpour.

At Huntly Lodge, the home of the Duke of Gordon, the head gardener, Mr Murdoch, reported that over 3¾ inches of rain fell between 5am on 3rd August and 5am on 4th August. This figure equalled one sixth of the annual rainfall for the whole of Moray.

In the Glen of Streams, the River Findhorn thundered downwards, sweeping away the bridge at Dulsie where the level had risen 40 ft above normal. The bridge at Ardclach was submerged, and though the high Daltulich Bridge was still standing, trees were torn from surrounding banks. At Relugas, a gardener had strange luck, catching a large salmon with his umbrella! Here the river had risen 50 ft above its banks.

Where the Findhorn and its tributary the Divie met, waves 20ft high reared into the air, tearing away bridges and buildings as the waters rushed down past Logie. The ancient tournament fields, the Medes of St John, were totally submerged. Only one more obstacle stood in the path of the surging river before it reached the sea, the beautiful Bridge of Findhorn, built 30 years previously of fine stone with three high arches. In one wild sweep it was gone, crumbling like a giant sandcastle, and again adding to the debris being swept towards the open Firth.

Reports of disaster came from all around. The tributaries of the River Spey added to the damage. The River Alness flooded the Estates of Teaninich, and the River Beauly submerged the whole area of Strathglass. The Duke of Gordon's tenants at the Ellie, below Orton, fled from their hamlet, or "bourach o hooses" as it was called, and took shelter in a neighbour's cottage. This was the home of John Geddes and on slightly higher ground, unlike their own houses which stood only 6 ft above the normal river level. During the previous floods in 1768 and '99 this cottage had been the only one to escape.

That Monday night, about 7pm, nine men, one woman and four children huddled together over the fire in their dripping clothes. They were all quite confident about their safety until Mr Geddes and a Mr Forsyth went out to batten down the stable door. They were alarmed to see how the flood had risen and before long, the water began to seep beneath the door. They had to lift food sacks and the meal chest on to a table while the woman and children took refuge on the box-bed. John Geddes lifted the embers from the fire, placed them on the girdle hanging above the grate, and put the oil lamp on a high wall shelf. Then he and the other men climbed on to any available tables and chairs.

Within an hour, the water had risen enough to extinguish the fire, and chairs had to be put upon the bed to keep the woman and children dry. After that, the only solution was to cut away the ceiling above the bed to give headroom, and they were seated on an old door placed across the backs of two chairs. Mr Geddes worked hard to keep them all safe, holding an axe handy in case he'd have to cut away the roof timbers as an escape route. At 2am, the lamp went out when it floated off the shelf, leaving them in total darkness, convinced that their end had come. However, they were eventually rescued from the rooftop by boat three hours later.

Each hour brought new devastation. The village of Dallas was flooded by the normally placid waters of the River Lossie, and the main street took on the appearance of a grand canal. Elgin was totally surrounded by water, looking like a city built on an island. The bridge at Bishopmill collapsed, and nearer to the mouth of the Lossie, the flood and tide waters combined, blotting out miles of reclaimed land to effect a complete, though temporary, restoration of the long-lost Loch of Spynie.

Beyond Ballindalloch, the River Spey had burst over the rich land of its own valley. By 5pm on that Monday afternoon, the water was pouring through the streets of Rothes and at nightfall the bridge in the centre of the town collapsed. A night of fear and apprehension followed, though luckily few lives were lost. Next day, it could be seen that at least 15 of the stoutly-

Fleeing from the floods ....

built houses had been completely demolished.

That same morning, Tuesday 4th August, a crowd had gathered on the bridge at Fochabers. This was a very solid structure with four wide arches, and the onlookers felt they could view the surging waters from comparative safety. The expanse of water was two miles wide in some places, and stretched over ten miles to the foot of Ben Aigen. Floating wreckage of all kinds tossed about on the surface, battering the supports of the bridge as it swept on to the sea. As the hours passed, it seemed certain that the bridge would withstand the onslaught, but at noon a small crack, no wider than an inch, appeared on the roadway. The people fled in panic and as they ran, the crack suddenly widened. Those watching from the banks gave a cry of horror as a young man was caught by a falling parapet and swept with the collapsing rubble into the torrent.

Meanwhile, in Garmouth and Kingston, at the mouth of the Spey, apprehension was slightly slower in growing. Having experienced much flooding in past years, the villagers had learned to live with this ever-present danger, and were perhaps just a little complacent. Much of the land around the two communities was under water by 7pm on the Monday evening, yet few people were alarmed. Attitudes changed, however, when the incoming tide at Kingston began to form mountainous waves as it was rebuffed by the onward-rushing river and the village looked certain to be destroyed.

The houses in the lower part of Garmouth were flooded by midnight, yet higher up the main street, most of the villagers were still in bed, and those who were aware of the mounting danger had great difficulty in persuading them to leave. The first building collapsed at 2am and those who had been in doubt needed no further urging. Many jumped from bed to find themselves knee-deep in water, their furniture floating around them.

Lights appeared in windows and in the streets, and the panic rose. Distress signals flashed from the ships in both harbours, and frantic parents could be heard screaming for their children. Men were soon wading waist-deep through the narrow streets, carrying half-dressed women and children, crying above the howling gale, the crashing masonry, cracking timber and rumbling carts.

In daylight, the full extent of the damage became apparent. It was an awesome sight. As far as the eye could see, the surrounding plains were covered by water. On the beaches lay stranded ships, masses of timber from the woodyards and shipyards, hundreds of dead farm and domestic animals, all kinds of household goods and furniture. Against all odds, hundreds of rabbits, toads and other small creatures were found alive clinging to the tops of the trees.

The view from the harbour at Kingston was dreadful. The schooner *Pursuit* had been torn from her moorings, and stranded out on the bar. The *Barbara Ann* had also gone adrift, carrying the *Unity* with her. One had been driven ashore inside the bar, the other, with no-one on board, had been swept to sea, then driven eastward, and finally thrown up on the beach. The *Elizabeth* held fast at her moorings, then capsized, her crew managing to jump to safety at the last moment.

Two more ships went aground between the Spey and Portgordon, and two others, the *Lizard* and the *Lively* which had sailed from Leith together, were stranded only ten yards apart. The *Robert of Limekilns* foundered just beyond the Spey Bay, and all on board were lost. Fortunately, there were no other fatalities, and most of the other vessels were later salvaged successfully.

Such was the devastation throughout the region that many people were sure it was God seeking vengeance with the return of the Great Flood.

By Wednesday morning, the skies had cleared, and people began to salvage what they could from the wreckage of their homes.

Boats of all kinds plied back and forth rescuing the stranded from rooftops and floating timbers. Householders were found perched high on sod roofs clutching bedraggled hens and chickens, as these were of more value than any personal belongings. One crofter had managed to store his pigs and several young calves in the hay loft of his byre, though the subsequent evacuation of these frightened animals into the small boats was no easy task. As more and more people were found, it became apparent that, amazingly, few had perished in the floods.

One of the strangest sights was when the fishing fleet set sail from Findhorn on rescue missions inland. The skippers kept logs as though setting out to sea, and the following extract was taken from that of the *Nancy:*—

"In danger of foundering from trees, and other landwrack running foul of us. Set all sails, scudded with a fair wind over Mr Davidson's farm, steered for a small house on the Estate of Tannachy. Rory Fraser, his daughter and two laddies were landed aboard. Made sail for Mr Williamson's farm, sounding all the way across the fields. Got to the house about noon. Mrs Williamson and three bairns were safely dry-docked on chairs on a bed. Bore up, steered a south-west course, passed over dykes and cornfields, made for Rotterford. Currents nearly swamped us. Neared the house and hailed, at last heard voices within. Found John, his wife and two other women. Got them on board safe, but fair drookit. We then stood up for Edgefield, sailed down the Market Green of Forres, got back to our mooring at Findhorn about 7pm".

Throughout the days following, there were many brave rescues by fishermen and villagers, for as always in times of severe disaster, people banded together doing what they could for one another. Flood relief funds were set up for destitute victims, but as so many had been affected, there was little enough to go round.

It took many years for the area to recover financially. Much of the rich soil on agricultural land had been swept away leaving it useless for many years to come, and the commercial ports of Kingston and Garmouth were so altered by the flood that they were no longer safe harbours, and were never used again. Even the salmon fisheries at the mouth of the Spey, once a rich source of industry, never regained their prosperity.

Perhaps, despite the severe winters of the past few years, we should look back, pause, and be thankful not to have such disastrous summers!

The Wee Folk o' the Borders
BY DAVID FERGUS

When did the fairy folk desert the Borders? Was it when the first train went snorting along the Waverley Route in the 1840s? Or did they linger on until the Education Act of 1872 finally drove them back "to Italy, whaur the deil, the witches, brownies and fairies dwal"?

Whatever the reason for their disappearance, there are few eye-witness accounts of the wee folk in the Borders after the middle of Queen Victoria's reign.

Lady John Scott, who wrote "Annie Laurie", was a firm believer in fairies and made an annual gift of a green dress to one of her servant lasses who claimed to have seen the guid neibours in the vicinity of Spottiswoode

A cowherd tries to grip the "wee creature" with red-hot tongs

sometime in the second half of the nineteenth century. Spottiswoode, on the southern edge of the Lammermuirs, was a remote district and it seems that the fairies still frequented its woods and mosses long after they had deserted other parts of the Borders.

Many a Borderer in the old days could — and did — tell of meetings with the wee folk. The last fairy to be seen in Wauchope Forest was described as "a little wee creaturie, aa clad in green, and wi lang hair, yellow as gowd hingin round its shouthers, nae bigger than a three-year-auld lassie, but feat and ticht, lith and limb as ony grown woman, and its face was the doonricht perfection o beauty".

This delectable creature appeared to one, Peter Oliver, as he was shepherding his ewes. Every hair on his head rose like the spines of a hedgehog but his visitor was pathetic rather than menacing, and kept repeating in a piteous voice, "Hae ye seen Hewie Milburn? Hae ye seen Hewie Milburn?" It followed Peter back to the farm at Hyndlee and came into the kitchen, still repeating its cry. The kitchen woman hospitably offered it some brose, which it refused, but when a loutish cowherd made as if to grip it with a pair of red-hot tongs, it understandably took offence, left the house and was never seen again.

It was in the same district, at the head of Rule Water, that another shepherd heard but did not see the fairy host. One fine summer night he went out to the hill to make sure that all was well with his flock. All was quiet, but "I heard a great plitch-platching as it were o hunders o little feet in the stream aboon the house. At first I was inclined to think it was the lambs, but then the grey licht o a simmer's nicht loot me see that nae lambs were there. I stayed and stood listenin and lookin, no kennin what to mak o't, whan aa at yince the plitch-platchin gae owre and than there was sic a queer eerie nicker, as o some hunders o creatures lauchin cam frae the upper linn, as left me in nae doubt that if fairies were still in the land, they were at the Swyrefoot that nicht".

Not all the Border fairies were as attractive as the mini-blonde of Hyndlee. Jenny Rogers, the wife of a coachman at Yair, saw fairies at Ashiesteel and said that they "had black faces and wee green coaties, and they nickered and leuch and danced". These same negroid faces turned up one Sunday at the cottage of Will Hadden, the factotum at Ashiesteel. They came and peered noisily in at the window of his cottage near the mansion. He chased them away and they disappeared in the haugh.

Although the country folk tried to placate the fairies by referring to them as "guid neibours", it was recognised that they could be very unpleasant neighbours indeed, mischievous at the best and often downright malevolent. They were especially dangerous to babies and young children. There was the case of the baby at Minto Crags whose mother was out gathering sticks in the woods under the cliffs that are crowned by Fatlips Castle. She was incautious enough to lay her baby by the side of a bush for a few moments and when she returned she was horrified at the child's wan and emaciated appearance. It was "aa begrutten owre" and cried incessantly so that when she took it home, she and her husband were forced to conclude that it was a changeling, left by the fairies who had kidnapped her own bonnie bairn.

They sought the help of the minister of Bedrule, the Reverend Mr Bourland, who examined the child and confidently announced that it was no earthly baby. He sent the mother to gather some plants of witches' thimbles (foxgloves) and then boiled the flowers and leaves and poured some of the decoction into the baby's mouth. Finally, he placed the boiled leaves on the child's breast, wrapped it tightly in a blanket, put it in its cradle and carried it into a barn at the side of the cottage. The door was then locked and the minister gave strict orders that no attempt should be made to open it until he returned next day. The anxious parents kept guard over the barn all night, but they neither saw nor heard anything and there was no sound from the baby.

Next day Mr Bourland opened the door, and there in the cradle lay the baby that had been lost, smiling and in perfect health. This event can be dated approximately, as Mr Bourland was minister of Bedrule in the latter part of the seventeenth century.

Another changeling in the same district betrayed itself by its addiction to the bagpipes, a well-known fairy weakness. It seems that a woman in Teviotdale gave birth to a fine healthy baby. For the first few days after the birth she was careful to take precautions against a fairy kidnapping by keeping her husband's blue bonnet in the cradle beside the infant (a hank of red thread or a twig of rowan would have been equally effective). One night though, she forgot to put the bonnet in beside the baby, and in the morning when she awoke she found to her horror and disgust that the cradle was occupied by an ugly little monster, barely human in appearance. Like all changelings this monstrosity howled and girned without ceasing.

About a month after the kidnapping, she had to go out, and as the whip-the-cat (travelling tailor) was in the house, she asked him if he would keep an eye on the "baby" while she was away. Once she was gone, the creature in the cradle sat up and whispered slyly to the tailor, "If ye winna tell my mammy, I'll play ye a spring on the pipes". At this point the fairy took a set of beautiful miniature pipes from under the bedclothes and started to play. The fairy was an expert piper, but the tailor knew what to do. He snatched the creature from the cradle and threw it on the fire that was blazing in the ingle. The changeling flew up the chimney in a shower of sparks and there in the cradle lay the real baby, sound asleep.

Presumably the bagpipes that the fairies loved were the Lowland or Northumbrian variety, as it is hard to imagine the wee folk having the wind to blow the great Highland bagpipe. One old Borderer, described as "a credible and decent man", used to tell that when he was a schoolboy on his way to school he often used to see two little fairies, dressed in green, playing the pipes and dancing at one particular spot beside a river. They paid no heed to him, and he accepted them as part of the natural order of things.

The fairies could be guid neibours indeed if you did them a favour. Some two hundred years ago everybody in Jedburgh knew that a certain local man owed all his wealth and prosperity to the benevolence of the wee folk.

In his youth this man had been making his way from Jedburgh to Hawick market, and as he passed over the side of Ruberslaw, the hill that dominates the western end of Teviotdale, he was astonished by a sudden uproar of female voices, chattering, wailing, laughing and crying. He looked around fearfully, but he was alone on the bare hillside. From the confused babble of sounds the only words he could distinguish were: "Oh, there's a bairn born, but there's nae sark to pit on't". These words were repeated again and again until the traveller took the hint.

He stripped off his ragged shirt, threw it on the ground and saw it snatched up into the air by invisible hands. The wailing ceased and sounds of merrymaking filled the air. The poor man went on his way to the market where he bought a sheep at a bargain price. This sheep was the foundation of his fortune, for thereafter everything he touched prospered.

Similarly, Mrs Buckham, the farmer's wife at Bedrule, never went short of meal after befriending a fairy woman. She was busy in her kitchen early one morning when a little woman in green clothes came in and very politely asked for the loan of a cupful of meal. Mrs Buckham was wise enough to give her a cupful of barley meal, although she had little enough for herself. In a short time the woman in green returned with an equal quantity of meal which Mrs Buckham put in her meal-ark. From that cupful of fairy meal the guidwife of Bedrule baked as much bread as served her own family and the reapers throughout harvest-time, and when the harvest was over there was still meal in the ark.

One of the most bizarre "sightings" of the fairy folk occurred about the year 1720 at Dryburgh. The village school was undergoing repairs and the teacher and his pupils were accommodated in the parish church. Late on a fine summer's afternoon while the sun was shining bright and beautiful through the large western window, there was a shrill whistle and "instantly a myriad of tiny figures, dressed in green, rushed in through the window, passed in a train along the gallery, dancing over the pews with much agility and apparent merriment, and again as suddenly disappeared at the opposite end of the edifice". This phenomenon was witnessed by the teacher and the children, one of whom used to retell the event in later years. He was, we are told, "a man who could not possibly be suspected of wilful fiction".

One man who was more than usually well-acquaint with the fairies was Will Laidlaw, usually known as Will o Phaup, an ancestor of James Hogg the Ettrick Shepherd. Will had many encounters, both by day and by night, with the fairy folk who lived in the wild hill country around the head waters of the Ettrick.

Late one misty All Hallows Even he was returning home from his flock on the hill when he heard sounds of revelry coming from a deep cleuch. Creeping to the edge of the cleuch he looked down and saw what seemed to be a fairy picnic. The fairies, all female, were dressed in "green polonians and grass-green bonnets". (A polonian is defined in *Jamieson's Dictionary of the Scottish Language* as a greatcoat). They spotted him and called his name twice and he realised that if they named him a third time he might fall under a spell so he ran for his life. His "hair stood up like the birses on a soo's back and every bit of his body outside and in prickled as if it had been brunt wi nettles". Once home he assembled his family and said prayers, but did not tell of his adventure until many years later.

On another occasion three fairies appeared to him and asked him for a silver key. This must have been a case of mistaken identity, as Will had no key, and when he asked them in God's name where they had come from, they immediately disappeared.

Many of Will's friends, by the way, attributed his fairy sightings to his fondness for brandy at Moffat mart!

Sir Walter Scott was involved in a curious fairy adventure when he was Sheriff at Selkirk. A travelling puppet show was in the town and some local youths stole some of the figures from the shed where they were being kept. When they reached the outskirts of the town they became alarmed at what they had done and left the puppets lying by the roadside. These were discovered in the grey light of dawn by the farmer of Brig Haugh and he took them for fairies and raised the alarm. The thieves were caught and brought to trial before Sir Walter, who questioned the farmer as chief witness.

"What did you take them for?"

"I canna preceesely say what my thochts were".

"Come, come! Did you think they were fairies?"

"Why, I'll no deny that I did just gie a thocht that they micht be the guid neibours, for troth, they were verra grand little people".

Perhaps the most famous of all Border fairy tales is that of the little girl who disappeared in the woods of Plora, near Innerleithen. One day, somewhere about the year 1720, a cottager of Traquair was casting peats on an open space near the old grey mansion-house. As he worked he carried on a desultory conversation with his seven-year-old daughter, Jane, who was playing nearby. When the little girl failed to answer a question, the father looked up from his work and found that the child had disappeared. Throwing down his flaughter-spade*, he began a search of the peatmoss. The child was nowhere to be seen. Nor was she at home. Nobody had seen her.

The alarm was raised in the tiny village, and parties of men and boys set out to find the missing child. Day after day they ranged through the woods and dragged the pools in the Quair Water and the Tweed, but no trace was found of Jane. The searchers were not encouraged by the pessimistic attitude of the little girl's father. He was convinced that she would never be found. The place where she had disappeared was known to be "no canny". It was obvious that she had been carried off by the wee folk, and to keep on searching might antagonise them.

There were others in the village who did not share his defeatist views. If the child had indeed been carried off by the fairies, then supernatural help would be needed to win her back. Accordingly the minister of Innerleithen got in touch with the ministers of seven neighbouring parishes and arranged for prayers to be said the following Sunday in all their kirks.

One of the ministers concerned in this mass rescue bid was the Reverend Henry Davidson, minister of Gala. As a shrewd Calvanist, he prefaced his prayer with the apology: "If she is dead, God will forgive our sin in praying for the dead, as we do it in ignorance". Then he continued: "But if she is still alive, I will answer for it that all the devils in hell shall be unable to keep her". We are told that he prayed in such a manner that all his hearers trembled.

Invisible hearers must also have trembled, for on that very day, within an hour of the prayers, and nine miles from the doughty divine's kirk, the missing child was found in the woods of Plora. They took her home and questioned her. She could give no clear account of where she had been, but said she had never been hungry as her "mother" had come and fed her several times a day with bread and milk. In spite of this, the child had been eating bark from the trees when she had been found. Her skin had turned a bluish colour, but this wore off after a few weeks. The child grew up and married, but for the rest of her life she was noted for her melancholy.

This sad little story had its glorious sequel. For years the tale, with all its supernatural trappings, passed from mouth to mouth on Tweedside and in the Vales of Ettrick and Yarrow. It was one of the hundreds of ballads and legends that Mrs Hogg told her son James, and it was this tale of the lost lass of Traquair that was transformed by Hogg into that masterpiece of the literature of the uncanny — "Kilmeny".

What are we, nowadays, to make of these "authentic" fairy tales, all vouched for as Gospel truth by people "whose veracity none can impeach?" Fifty years ago very few self-respecting adults would have admitted to a belief in fairies. Fairy tales were for children only or for sober scholars (usually Teutonic) of comparative folklore. What of today? It seems to me that, thanks partly to the Tolkien cult, there are probably more professed fairy-believers now than at any time since the days of Will o Phaup.

Rationalists might say that these fairy tales reveal more about the tellers than about the fairies, and when we read these unsophisticated "eye-witness" accounts we may well agree with the great David Hume that the knavery and credulity of mankind can explain most supernatural happenings. It is certainly not difficult to explain away the fairies in the tales I have recounted. The question is, though, do you want to explain them away in terms of ailing babies (changelings), alcoholic visions (Will o Phaup's encounters), broken families (Jane of Plora)? Or would you rather believe in fairies?

footnote.... * A two-handed spade for cutting peats and turfs.

Tales of the Badenoch witches told around the fireside

BY NIALL M BROWNLIE

A farmer from Ralia in Inverness-shire was reputed to be a white witch, something he made no attempt to hide. To impress one of his neighbours that he possessed these benign powers, he would dress up in red, but the man looked on him more as an eccentric than someone with the *eolas* (knowledge).

He was said to have had the power to recover lost or stolen property, restore the milk yield to cows, make barren women fruitful and generally counteract the evil spells of black witches. That his services were in demand cannot be in doubt as the following short stories amply demonstrate.

A man in the district had some valuables stolen and he sent for the farmer to help him recover the missing property. Together they walked through the village, letting it be known that the red-coated farmer was there to seek out the stolen goods. They returned home late, and apparently without success, but, strange to say, when the man rose next morning, he found that all the missing articles had been replaced during the night.

Cows were particularly prone to the spells of black witches. The cow was a peasant's most valuable asset, being the main source of nourishment for the family, and if he fell from grace with his betters, they would hire the local witch to spirit away the milk yield. Stories of witches assuming the shapes of hares to suck cows are numberless throughout the Highlands and Islands.

He meets a man dressed in black riding a black horse ....

To ward off such evils, the white witch would suggest a variety of counter-charms: placing rowan branches above the byre door; tying a rowan twig to the cow's tail; or binding a ball of horse's hair round the handle of the *cuman* (milk-pail).

The rowan was reckoned to be the most powerful deterrent of all as the following translation of a Gaelic rhyme by the celebrated poet Ailean Dall (Blind Allan) of Glencoe suggests. Allan belonged to the age of the great Gaelic Bards, and died around 1830.

A tuft of rowan twigs
From the face of Ailsa Craig
Put a red thread and a knot on it,
And place it on the end of the sprinkler,
And though the witch of Endor· came,
Allan could manage her.

It followed that a man who could encourage the milk yield in cows could also help a barren woman. For a fee of one guinea, the farmer would visit the couple to perform mystic ceremonies such as the blessing of a potion of water with holy Latin incantations. This water was to be taken nightly until the desired results were obtained.

One of Badenoch's most famous and powerful witches was the Witch of Laggan, and although there are four places in Badenoch that bear the name Laggan, according to oral tradition, the witch came from Laggan Farm near Lynchat east of Kingussie.

This notorious daughter of Badenoch was known as *Bean an Lagain* (The Wife of Laggan), and near her croft was a township known as *Taigh na Camaisidh* (House of Camshie). There was constant feuding between the witch and the crofters of the township. A herdsman, whose croft was nearest to Laggan, suffered more than most, and was often annoyed by the caprices of the Wife of Laggan. One day, he found the Laggan sheep eating his grain and he drove them into a fank. As a condition of release, he demanded reparation from the witch. This she reluctantly agreed to, and on having paid for the damage, she vowed to have her revenge.

Shortly afterwards, the poor man's cow died mysteriously, his barn was burned down, and his home was constantly visited by an enormous and ferocious black cat. So many were the disasters that befell him and his family that they left the district.

It was then the turn of the crofters who had aided the herdsman to come in for the evil attention of the witch. Soon their misfortunes increased, and fear swept the township.

At last a replacement was found for the departed herdsman in the person of a local man called Donald Bane. Skilled in the arts of white witchcraft, he advised all the crofters to tie a sprig of bog fir either to the cows' tails or horns, to place rowan branches on the roofs of their byres, and a horseshoe above all the dwelling-house doors. These would offer protection from the influences of evil.

In spite of all this, the black cat continued to stalk the district, and hens, chickens and eggs frequently disappeared. Donald Bane began to suspect that the culprit was something more than just a cat, and he decided to go hunting. Loading his gun with a silver button, he went after the animal. On sighting it, he fired, wounding it in one of its hind legs. The cat let out a most unearthly and ear-piercing scream and immediately disappeared. The next time the Wife of Laggan was seen, she was limping badly.

Later the same year, Donald was up at the shieling. After a very wet day he was sitting by the fire drying his clothes when a black hen entered and took up position beside him. His dogs growled and Donald blessed himself. Then he noticed that the hen was getting bigger and bigger, until it assumed the form of the Witch of Laggan. She spoke to the herdsman, and suggested that his dogs were far too fierce. When she requested that they be tied, Donald replied that he had no string for the purpose. The witch then pulled out a few strands of hair from her head, and told him to use them instead.

Donald bent and pretended to do so, but, unseen by her, he put the hairs on the sleeve of his coat. Next moment the witch sprang at him like a wild cat. The dogs began to bark and she screamed "Tighten hairs, cut and strangle!". She was taken by surprise when the dogs pounced on her, bearing her to the ground and she just managed to struggle to her feet and rush out, hotly pursued by the ravening animals.

Next morning at dawn, Donald set off for home, and on the way he found one of his dogs dead with a piece of human flesh in its mouth. On arriving home he was told that the Wife of Laggan was dying.

When Donald related what had happened at the shieling, several men set out for the Laggan farmhouse. On arrival they were told that the witch had just passed away. The men went in and removed the body to the top of a round hillock nearby, where, without ceremony, it was burned to ashes. It is a remarkable fact that when trees were planted on the spot, none took root. The hillock became known as the Witch's Hill and on it today stands the War Memorial.

Badenoch's other famous witch was known as the Witch of Nuide. Nuide is situated between Ralia Bridge and Inverton and near Nuide are the remains of an old crofting township. Oral tradition says that it was here that the witch lived. She was feared far and wide and she exacted tribute in kind and money, and woe betide anyone who refused to pay. Their cows would dry up, their young stock would die off, and their farm buildings would be given over to the flames of Lucifer.

So powerful was the witch that men were afraid to leave their homes, or take part in any community life without her sanction or goodwill. However, a new tenant came to the district to occupy Ruthven Farm. He was a Lowlander, did not believe in witches, and refused to pay tribute. The witch threatened revenge, but he told her to go to the Devil and be damned for it.

One summer evening, he and his herdsman were watching their cattle in the meadows adjacent to his farm when they saw a strange sight. A hare was leaping from cow to cow, apparently sucking their milk. The farmer levelled his gun at the hare, fired, and the hare bounded away. The herdsman declared afterwards thet the hare had put a forepaw to its nose and jeered at them.

The farmer found later that the cows which had been touched by the hare went dry. Ragwort was blamed, and all the cows were removed to another field, but this made no difference. All the cattle became dry and some died. Then the farmer fell from a hay cart and broke his leg.

These unaccountable misfortunes followed so quickly upon each other that the farmer reluctantly gave in, grudgingly admitting that there might, after all, be an element of truth in witchcraft. To appease the witch, he sent his servant with a brace of fat duck saying, "Take these to the old hag, and I hope they choke her".

Later, before the end of the \next moon, the farmer went to the Newtonmore Fair. Normally he would have gone there by way of the Spey Ford, but the river was in spate so he made his way instead via Nuide, and over a bridge west of Ralia.

Darkness was falling before the fair ended, and the farmer set off home by the same route with his two fine collies as his only companions. After crossing Inverton Burn, the dogs started to growl fiercely and came from his left side to his right. He then became aware of a huge greyhound ready to spring. Scarcely had he time to bless himself when it leapt, flying at his throat. A hefty blow from his stick warded it off. The collies then attacked the hound and a fearful struggle ensued. It is said that the farmer heard agonised cries coming from a distance shouting "Call off your dogs!" He paid no heed, and fled, finally reaching home in a very exhausted state. Neither the dogs nor the witch were ever seen or heard of in Badenoch again.

The story had a strange sequel. A man from Strathdearn met a woman running, hotly pursued by two black dogs. As she passed, she asked him if she was far from Dalcrossie Churchyard. About three minutes later he met a man dressed in black, riding a black horse. The stranger asked the very same question. He also enquired if a woman had passed, pursued by two black dogs.

Legend has it that if a witch reaches Dalcrossie Churchyard, she is safe from the devil and eternal damnation. Our witch reached there.

Curiously, the actual location of this sanctuary has never been established.

★　★　★ ·· ★

The forest of Gaick lies high on the mountains south of the River Tromie. It is an eerie, desolate area, and has long been considered a place of evil. Within its recesses lies Loch Bhrodainn into which, it is said, the white stag of Ben Alder disappeared. Here, too, is Loch an Duin where a rash young lover from Atholl met a dreadful fate. On the rocky slopes of Loch an t-Seilich the wicked Red Comyn was torn to pieces as he walked along the drovers' path, and a very famous hunter called MacIan experienced here the last proof of the power and versatility of the famous Wife of Laggan. Badenoch has always associated Gaick with the supernatural as the following story illustrates.

Between Nuide and Gaick was a shieling called Ruighe Bhad Fearna (The Alder Clump Shieling). One night in 1799, the only occupants were a young mother, her children and a little servant girl named Anna. During the night they were very alarmed by sounds which suggested that the lonely shieling was surrounded by a crowd of people. When dawn came, they ventured forth, buut there was no trace of any nocturnal visitors. Anna was dispatched in haste to fetch the husband and he spent every evening with his wife and family in the shieling. This, I think, gives an excellent demonstration of how Badenoch looks upon Gaick.

★   ★   ★   ★

Many years ago, there was a notorious recruiting officer by the name of Captain John Macpherson living in Badenoch. This man was a great huntsman and he was known locally as the Oighre Dubh (Black Officer).

At the age of 70, this renowned but dreaded man decided to go hunting on Christmas Day and he invited a number of his friends to meet him at the house of the Post Bane (Fair-haired Post). When he got there, none of those invited had come. Post Bane suggested postponement, but the Oighre Dubh was determined to carry out his plan and they set out for Gaick.

Reaching a bothy, they settled down for the night. Their dogs were very restive and had to be tied to the bed post. In the early hours of the morning a knock came to the door, and the Captain answered it. He slipped out shutting the door behind him. The Post Bane was puzzled by this and got up to have a look. In the half light he caught a glimpse of a dark figure, talking to the Black Officer, and he heard voices raised. Then he heard the Captain saying, "I will be here one year from tonight, and I will bring a number of freinds with me", and without another word he returned to the bothy. He looked pale and he told his companion that the caller was one of the invited guests who was extremely angry at the others' failure to appear.

In the morning, Post Bane searched for foot or hoof prints, but there were none. When he got home, the Post related his experiences and the people of the district became convinced that the Oighre Dubh was in league with the evil spirit of Gaick.

A year later, it was learned that the Black Officer was arranging for another hunting expedition to Gaick. Many refused his invitation to join him, but at last he set out on Christmas Eve accompanied by four brave souls. Later, another party of eight headed by Bane's son, on whom the Black Officer exerted a very strong influence, set off for the bothy at Gaick. Near Nuide, the young leader lost not only the uppers, but the soles of his shoes. This was considered an evil portent and the party returned home.

There they waited in vain for the advance party's return. At last, an old soldier volunteered to lead a search for the lost hunters. They reached the bothy of Gaick to find it in ruins. In the rubble were the bodies of the Captain's four companions and, much farther away, they found the body of the Oighre Dubh. They set off home, a mournful procession headed by the body of the Black Officer.

As they descended the hill, a fierce storm arose, making progress impossible. They halted and in desperation and fear for their lives, the old soldier yelled, "Put the old devil's remains to the rear".

They did as instructed, the storm abated, and the party reached home in safety.

That story leaves us with several questions. Who was the nocturnal visitor to the bothy the previous year? Was he man or woman, witch or wizard — or was he the Devil himself? Was the Black Officer in league with some evil spirit who eventually claimed the lives of him and his companions? Who can tell?

footnote...   *First Book of Samuel, Chapter 28, verse 7.

The search for Mons Graupius
BY GORDON MAXWELL

It is something of a tragedy that the scene of the first major conflict record-ed on Scottish soil should remain unknown. It took place just over 1,900 years ago, in the early autumn of A.D.83 (or just possibly 84), when the massed levies of Caledonia met a Roman expeditionary force at a site known as Mons Graupius.

What scanty knowledge we have of this battle we owe to the fact that the commander of the Roman Army in Britain, Gnaeus Julius Agricola, had recently given his daughter in marriage to a young man destined to be one of Rome's most distinguished historians, Publius Cornelius Tacitus.

One of the first major works to be written by Tacitus was a biography of his father-in-law, in which there is not only an account of the exploits of Agricola during his six-year governorship of the Roman province of Britan-nia, but also a summary of Roman operations in Britain from the forays of Julius Caesar in 55 and 54 B.C. until Agricola's arrival as governor in A.D.77 or 78.

According to Tacitus, the permanent occupation of the province began in A.D.43 under the Emperor Claudius, and although most of the lowland zone was swiftly overrun, it took almost 35 years before Roman armies stood poised to enter what is now known as Scotland.

At that time, of course, the inhabitants were not Scots (the Scoti did not migrate from their home in Ireland until several centuries later); the Romans knew them collectively as Britanni and they were a group of Celtic-speaking peoples not greatly different in culture from their neighbours to the south. Ancient geographers recorded the names of in-dividual tribes — the Votadini of Lothian and the Merse, for example, and the Dumnonii of Strathclyde and Central Scotland — but Tacitus, who was no great user of proper names, suggests that the people living to the north of the Forth, in the region he called Caledonia, were a relatively homogeneous group. In later times, under the name Caledonii, these people apparently formed one of the two major portions of the nation that passed into history as the Picts.

If we are to believe Tacitus, the campaigns of Agricola were attended by almost uninterrupted success. A year and a half after he took office, he had quenched the last flames of resistance in North Wales and had seized the whole of northern England in a grip of steel.

His third annual campaign led him into virgin territory, Roman col-umns striking unopposed to the north of the Forth, perhaps even as far as the Tay. The two subsequent seasons witnessed the consolidation of the Forth-Clyde isthmus as a temporary frontier, while south-west Scotland was subdued and the western sea-routes were thoroughly explored, possibly with the intention of armed reconnaissance of Ireland.

In the sixth season, the northward advance was resumed, the enemy now being clearly identified as the nations living across the Forth in Caledonia. The native Britons showed their metttle at an early stage by launching a determined assault on the weakest of Agricola's battle-groups, the Ninth Legion; their ultimate objective was doubtless to penetrate the

Clash of swords!

screen of legions and invade the recently-conquered territory to the south; perhaps they hoped to cut Roman supply-lines and rally the southern tribes to their cause. It was not to be. Agricola got wind of the enemy plans and, by dint of a forced march at night, came upon them just as they were beginning to force their way into the Ninth Legion's defended bivouac.

From the fierce fighting that followed, probably somewhere between the Earn and the Tay, both sides were able to extract some credit, and neither felt that its hopes of eventual victory had been in any way dimmed. The scene was thus set for the final conflict.

The last momentous year of campaigning began with personal tragedy for Agricola, when he lost his infant son. In the midst of his grief he threw himself into preparations for the coming battle. He knew from his scouts that the warriors of Caledonia were determined to stand and fight. They had chosen the place, and perhaps its location had been deliberately "leaked" by the Britons who wanted no more indecisive fencing. Every nation of the north had sworn to support the cause, sending its young fighting men and hardened veterans to assemble at a hill or mountain called by Tacitus, Mons Graupius.

By the time Agricola's troops arrived on the field, there were more than 30,000 Caledonians under arms; the Roman strength, it has been calculated, was somewhat less than this, but probably not much and certainly not unusually weak for an expeditionary force that had had to move with speed against a rapidly-growing threat. In any case, numbers were not so important as quality. And quality in terms of training, discipline, and equipment was what the Roman military machine possessed in abundance — as the events of the day made hideously apparent.

At first, both commanders are reported to have addressed their respective armies.

Agricola's exhortation seems weak, if not downright discouraging: "A noble death is preferable to survival with shame, and yet both safety and honour may depend on the same course of action. Indeed it will be no dishonour to fall here at the very edge of the world".

The words of Calgacus, however, would strike sparks from the coldest heart: "Here is your true leader, here your country's army. Yonder lie all the trappings of slavery — tribute and forced labour — and it is this battlefield which will decide whether you endure them forever or instantly banish them. Now off to your lines! Be true to your ancestry and think of your children's children!"

Calgacus, the name that Tacitus gives the Caledonian leader, although presumably a Latinisation of a Celtic word *calgach* (swordsman), is little more than a title. Yet the words that are put into his mouth, the condemnations of imperialist greed, the contempt for political "weasel-words" ("The Peace which Romans talk so much about is the Peace that goes with Desolation"), the appeals to love of liberty and ties of blood, cannot be wholly different from the real message which inspired the Caledonian host that day.

It is tantalising that Tacitus has little to say about the scene of the battle. That it lay deep within enemy territory has been presumed because the battle was not fought until the very end of the campaigning season. Agricola's reported description of its location is "the very edge of the natural world" — in other words, "the back of beyond". But whether it lay two or 20 days march north of Roman-held territory cannot be deduced from the Tacitus account.

We know as little about the character of the site as we do of its geographical location. The Caledonian forces are said to have occupied a hill, doubtless one commanding an important land-route and probably on the southern limits of an extensive tribal domain, but it is impossible to tell if it was a large and impressive feature or merely a conspicuous hillock which gave its name to a larger area round about. The Celtic word *craup* which may lie behind the Latin *Graupius* could refer, it has been argued, to a craggy peak or a rounded summit of any size. The Grampian hills, which are named after it, owe their spelling to an error by one of the earliest editors of Tacitus.

There were six distinct phases in the combat which followed the ordering of the opposed battle-lines. At first, the British chariots skirmished in the level ground which lay between the two armies; then both sides exchanged volleys of spears and javelins before coming to grips. For the Romans this meant advancing uphill against the tightly-packed ranks of the native levies, but the auxiliary infantry, with their better discipline, soon began to make headway, while the Caledonian warriors discovered that the long slashing swords that were their accustomed weapons, were too unwieldy in close-quarter work. The stabbing and cutting of the shorter Roman swords were cruelly effective.

Nevertheless, even though Agricola's infantry was now joined by cavalry (who had just seen off the skirmishing charioteers), the impetus of the Roman advance began to slow down, as the soldiers found they had also to contend with the steepness of ground already encumbered with piles of dead and wounded.

Surveying the fray from higher up on Mons Graupius, Calgacus now ordered in his reserves; round the flanks of the struggling troops he sent them to fall upon the apparently undefended Roman rear. But it was to deal with sudden threats like this that Agricola had kept four regiments of horse, possibly concealing them in nearby cover. With little difficulty they scattered the Caledonian reserves and then turned upon the main body of the enemy with dreadful effect. Before long the Britons broke and fled, no longer united in a common cause, but seeking now the salvation of none but themselves and their own kin, or at most their clan.

So complete did the victory appear that some of the Roman troops abandoned their discipline and gave pursuit, one party in doing so, coming close to getting ambushed in the woodland that adjoined the battlefield. At the end of the day, Roman casualties were slight, no more than 360 men from the auxiliary forces losing their lives. So overwhelming had been

Roman superiority that Agricola had not needed to call upon the legionary reserve. British losses, on the other hand, were disastrously high; Tacitus put them at 10,000 or almost 30 per cent of their total strength.

Although it is notoriously difficult to assess the accuracy of casualty figures given in accounts of any conflict (even in modern times), the proportions are not improbable. An appropriate parallel is Culloden, where, as at Mons Graupius, courage and fervour failed to enable a poorly equipped, less cohesive force to stand against one enjoying superiority of equipment and training. The losses there on either side were similarly contrasting. At the close of the battle, the scene which presented itself to Agricola resembled in many details that surveyed centuries later by Cumberland: "On all sides there lay abandoned weapons, bodies of the slain, and mutilated limbs; everywhere the ground was soaked with blood".

There can be no doubt, even when due allowance is made for any exaggeration in which a Roman historian may have indulged, that this was a clear-cut victory for Agricola's men. It may equally be recognised as a decisive victory, for although Agricola did not choose to march further into Caledonia, there was little to prevent him doing so, had he wished — apart from the approach of winter. Instead, at a leisurely pace he retired to more southerly quarters. Within a few months he had resigned the governorship and made his way back to Rome, leaving his successor to consolidate his conquests and construct permanant bases for the garrison of the newly-extended province.

Ironically, less than five years later, Roman frontier-policy in Britain underwent a thoroughgoing reappraisal, and much of the territory for which Agricola's army had laboured and fought was abandoned. Before 20 more years had passed, the frontier stood on the Tyne-Solway isthmus, and every Roman site in Scotland had been demolished and given up. One wonders what the survivors of Mons Graupius, on either side, felt about these vagaries of fortune.

Later generations have had mixed views on the achievements of the Romans in Scotland. On the one hand there is an evident pride that the former inhabitants of what is now Scotland were such redoubtable opponents of the mighty Roman Empire that it took numerous campaigns and two mighty frontier walls to keep them in check. Many have been swift to make comparisons between the struggle for freedom against the power of Rome and the fight for independence from England. On the other hand, Scottish antiquaries have not been slow to preen themselves on their country's possession of the remarkable, if not unique, monuments to imperial greatness that were erected by Agricola and his successors; there may be no amphitheatres or aqueducts, but we take a perverse pleasure in mouldering ramparts and half-choked ditches — the symbols of foreign domination — proudly pointing out that they were made by soldiers at the farthest limit of their power, on the very fringes of the known world.

Both these factors have contributed to a continuing curiosity about the actual location of Mons Graupius. The earliest researchers had little to work upon beyond the bare text of Tacitus, but they supplied the want with ready use of their imaginations. Thus, in the early 16th centrury, Hector Boece's *Chronicles of Scotland* presented a most unhistorical clanjamfry of Picts, Danes and Scots, under the command of "Galdus", meeting Agricola's legions in the shadow of the "mountanis of Granzeben". He seems to suggest that the armies clashed some way to the north of "ane rich town of the Pychtis callit Inchetuthill" on the banks of the Tay, a little way below Dunkeld.

In the midst of this farrago of invention there are nuggets of fact: Inchtuthill really did exist in the late 1st century A.D., but it was a Roman military site, for a short while the 50-acre base of the Twentieth Legion; its occupation in some form may have been crucial to the tactics adopted by Agricola in his campaign against the Caledonian confederacy, but modern excavation has suggested that a permanent garrison was not established here until the governorship of Agricola's successor.

Nevertheless, historians were slow to abandon the attractive equation first outlined by Boece, and the numerous impressive earthworks in the area surrounding Inchtuthill were woven by later embellishers into a richly detailed, if fanciful, reconstruction of the battle. The medieval deer-fence, Buzzart Dykes, on Cochrage Muir north-west of Blairgowrie, became "the Caledonian camp" and the adjacent prehistoric cairnfield the cemetery which received the British dead.

Most later antiquaries felt compelled to take a more objective view, as research and fieldwork gradually revealed the difference between Roman military works and native fortifications. Ironically, the first real progress was made by army officers engaged in the military survey of North Britain after the failure of the '45, men who could appreciate at first hand the tactical and strategic problems facing an army of occupation. Foremost among these were William Roy, the father of the Ordnance Survey, and Robert Melville, who discovered and planned many of the great marching camps built by the Romans in successive campaigns in Scotland. Between them they identified about a dozen camps that extended in a long arc from Ardoch, some seven miles south of Crieff, to Glenmailen on the River Ythan near Huntly.

Yet even Roy could not do better than conjecture which of these sites might be identified with the bivouac of Agricola's troops before Mons Graupius. He, too, resorted to the traditional use of place-names, suggesting that Battledykes, Oathlaw, to the north of Forfar, was a possible candidate, the battlefield itself being on the nearest foothills of the Grampian massif; Cat Law, betwen Glen Isla and Glen Prosen, and dubiously derived from the Gaelic *cath*, "a battle", offered persuasive support.

Roy himself rejected this identification, however, and trusting rather to his skill in reading terrain, eventually proposed that the site should be sought nearer the north-east end of Strathmore, where the mountains came closest to the coast and the British "could force Agricola to fight on their own terms". Had he lived to visit the Roman camp at Raedykes near

Stonehaven, Roy would almost certainly have supported the vigorous claims that were later made for its recognition as the long-lost site; indeed, arguments in\ its favour were still being advanced by archaeologists 150 years after Roy's death.

And well they might, for the intervening period had seen little serious study of Roman campaigning-works; witness the famous episode in Scott's *Antiquary*, where Jonathan Oldbuck's identification of "the Kaim of Kinprunes" as Agricola's camp at Mons Graupius is ridiculed by Edie Ochiltree: "Praetorian here, praetorian there; I mind the bigging o't!" The lack of fruitful research did not stop enthusiasts advancing various ingenious theories about the location. At the beginning of the 19th century, the Rev Andrew Small and Lt-Col Miller composed colourful scenarios for an action that unrolled near Meralsford in Fife, beneath the frowning northern slopes of the Lomond Hills: and in 1935, Pitblado tried to turn history on its head not merely by suggesting that the great battle was fought on the golf-course at Gleneagles, but by insisting that it was, in effect, a Roman defeat, not a victory. He supported this claim by arguing that the Tacitean figure of 360 fatalities on Agricola's side referred solely to casualties among Roman-born officers; hence, on the assumption that other ranks suffered in proportion, total Roman losses were of the order of 30,000!

In short, no real progress could be made until some means was found of identifying Roman marching-camps of the Agricolan period and relating them to the respective phases of the invasion as recounted by Tacitus. This requirement was at last amply supplied with the advent of aerial photography. Survey from the air has gradually uncovered many of the lost treasures of our archaeological heritage. Monuments which have been worn away by centuries of agriculture and decay, until they are practically invisible at ground level, may be located by the aerial surveyor through the characteristic crop-markings which they generate. Roman sites, by reason of their regular plan, are particularly susceptible to this means of identification and study, and in the past 50 years aerial prospecting has revolutionised our knowledge of Roman Scotland.

Most of the research on marching-camps has been carried out by Professor J.K.S.St Joseph of Cambridge University, who has identified amongst the scores of Roman sites photographed from the air a number of distinct categories. Some of these may be assigned with a fair degree of certainty to the late 1st century A.D., but it is still impossible to be absolutely sure that they housed the armies of Agricola. Nevertheless, there is one group, whose gates are defended by a curious combination of curving and oblique outworks — first photographed at Stracathro near Edzell — which seems a very likely candidate for that honour. They range widely in size (from about three to 60 acres) and are found in nearly all parts of Scotland penetrated by the Romans, from Beattock in Annandale to Auchinhove near Huntly. Yet, with this wide distribution and variety, they clearly cannot be said to indicate a single line of march. Moreover, the larger and more uniformly-sized series first identified by Roy and his contemporaries, and now supplemented by numerous aerial discoveries which certainly do represent the progress of legions on the march, are now mostly thought to date to the early 3rd century A.D.

The only reliable evidence for large-scale troop movements, such as might have occurred during Agricola's campaigns, is provided by the two square camps of about 115 acres on the south side of Strathearn at Dunning and Abernethy — about a day's march apart; a late 1st century date is proved by pottery\ found in the ditch of one example. It may be presumed that the most likely occasion for such operations in such massive strength — probably the whole of Agricola's field-force — would have been the initial thrust to the Tay; the suggestion has nevertheless been made that the hill of Duncrub, in the vicinity of Dunning, is the historical Mons Graupius although the link is purely etymological!

What can safely be argued is that camps of a similar size or larger would have been needed to accommodate the force which Agricola took with him to meet Calgacus. Hence the attraction of the argument recently advanced by Professor St.Joseph that the arc of large camps that extends from Raedykes to the Pass of Grange indicates the route followed by Agricola on that last campaign.

The camps of this group vary slightly in size, but, with one exception, approximate to 110 acres. The odd man out, Logie Durno, to the north-west of Inverurie, is 144 acres in size, and it lies more or less at the foot of that conspicuous peak Bennachie. The greater size of the camp suggests that there was a particular reason for the temporary concentration of Roman forces at this point, a similar, otherwise independent, unit now being brigaded together with the main body. Was that reason the presence of Calgacus and the Caledonian host on nearby Bennachie?

So was Mons Graupius none other than our old friend Bennachie? The argument has much in its favour although there are still problems: the date of the camp in question has yet to be proved and the occurrence of a battle beside it still to be substantiated, whether by mass graves or caches of broken weapons.

Amidst much that is open to debate, one thing remains certain: the passing of years will not dull the archaeologist's enthusiasm or the general public's curiosity about the first recorded battle for Caledonia!

Scottish Stories
of the
Supernatural

How Lady Fiona was wounded by a ghost

There are not many instances whereby anyone is marked or hurt by a paranormal situation, but there are some, and here I will tell of an occasion where this did occur.

It involved a landed, aristocratic family and took place in the days before radio, or even telephone, and I shall refer to the main participants as Lord Alistair and Lady Fiona, who were brother and sister.

Orphaned at an early age, they grew up with a very strong affection for each other. This continued long after they had been separated and they made a mutual promise that whatever of them should die first then he or she, if possible, would come back and appear to the other.

Ultimately, Lady Fiona married a Baronet, whom I shall call Sir Andrew, but she still made fairly frequent visits back to visit her brother.

The marriage was a very happy one but one morning Sir Andrew was very distressed as his wife came down to breakfast showing obvious signs of having experienced a very restless night.

Her face was pale and drawn, her eyes listless and dull, while her manner was so tense that it suggested her having been subject to some frightening ordeal.

Try as he might, though, she would not give him any information as to the cause, in fact, she persisted in claiming that she was perfectly well and there was nothing untoward.

He was particularly inquisitive about her wrist, which was bound by a roll of ribbon, but she would say absolutely nothing about any wound or injury.

"Please don't keep on asking me, dear Andrew, about this ribbon. All I can tell you is that you will never see me without it".

"Can't I take you to a physician? . . . Surely . . ."

"If it was as simple as that, I would obviously let you, and if it was something that concerned our married life, I would certainly tell you; but it doesn't, and I can only ask that you will trust me and respect my silence".

"But you never before refused me a request".

"That's true . . . so I just beg you not to ask me any more about this".

"It'll be as you wish . . . but only as long as you promise that there is nothing I, or anyone else, can do to help".

"Of that, I certainly do assure you".

During the meal she was certainly very tense and made only a pretence of taking any food. She also asked several times if the post had been delivered.

"Are you expecting something important?" he ultimately asked.

"Yes", she answered and, after some hesitation added: "I'm about to hear that my dear brother, Alistair, has died. It happened two days ago at four o'clock in the afternoon".

"You've had a bad dream. That's what has upset you".

Shortly afterwards a maid came in with some letters and she quickly selected one particular envelope from the batch, opened it and read the contents before looking over at her husband.

"It's as I said. It happened almost exactly at four o'clock".

Sir Andrew himself lived for only a few years after that and died, leaving her with three of a family, the youngest being the only boy.

Following his death she led the life of a virtual recluse, never appearing at any of the County functions and rarely visiting friends, but she always persisted in having the ribbon cover her wrist.

Time went on, and there came an occasion when Lady Fiona surprised some friends by sending invitations asking them to spend a day with her; amongst them was a lifetime associate, whom I shall call Lady Huina, and during that day she adjourned to her bedroom for a time and asked this lady to accompany her, also sending for her son to join them.

Putting both on their strictest confidence, she started off by telling them that she was sure that she had not long to live, and told them the following tale.

"One night, while Andrew was still alive, I awoke with the sensation that there was someone in the room, and gradually I was able to discern the form of my brother, Lord Alistair, standing near my bed.

I tried vainly to awaken my husband but he slept on as if he was in a coma, and in the meantime my visitor started to talk. He told me that he had died at four o'clock on the previous day and that he had been permitted to come to me as we once agreed by mutual promise.

'First of all', he continued, 'the child to which you will soon give birth will be a son, who will one day marry my daughter, but not many more years will pass away before your life will enter a period of great loneliness'. He then told me of temptation and other things that could happen after that and that my life would end in my forty-seventh year.

'My goodness gracious . . . can I not do something about this?' I asked.

'You can indeed, you have free will and you are in no way compelled to act in any particular way'.

She was, of course, much upset at these revelations and, after a period of silence between them, inquired how, in the morning, she would be sure that it was really his ghost that had been there, and that it was not all a figment of her imagination.

'The news of my death is already in the post to you. Surely that will be proof enough'.

'Not really. I could be the recipient of some form of precognition, either through a dream, or from some other kind of subconscious thought'.

'See, I will disarrange the canopy at the top of your bedrail. That could not be done without a set of steps, or better still, here is your diary. I'll write something in the space allotted to this particular day.'

'I'm very familiar with your handwriting. Even in sleep, I think I could do a fair imitation of it'.

'Well, be that as it may, but I'm not allowed to touch you because I would do you a lasting injury'.

A night visitor for Lady Fiona

'I don't mind a slight mark, or even a small scar'.

'You have always had great courage. Then hold out your hand'.

He proceeded to touch her wrist, and it felt like being pierced by an icicle, cold and hard, as frozen marble, while the sinews shrunk up into an abrasion of scarred tissue.

'Now, no living person must ever look at that mark on your wrist'. Then, turning away, he vanished.

During the conversation she had been reasonably composed, and she then again tried to awake her husband, but without success.

Then, looking around the room, she noticed that the canopy curtain on the high rail was in slight disarray, while her diary was opened and contained writing on the space for this particular day.

Locking it away in her bureau, she then looked around for some ribbon which she wound over the mark on her wrist.

Her child, who was born later that year, was a boy, and four years later her husband died. Then came the years of mournng and loneliness and a period of temptation, vexation and sadness, followed by spells of deep depression.

"I called you here today because I am now well into my forty-seventh year. It was one of the points that was made, which have not yet come to pass, so I am now convinced that I am within a few months of death.

When I do die . . . I want you, Huina, to unbind my wrist before my son here, and you'll each see the visible proof of what I've been telling you about".

She then turned to her son and spoke confidentially to him for a time before entreating him to marry his cousin, Lord Alistair's daughter, as had also been decreed during the apparition.

Then she lay back on the pillows, as if she was now very tired, and told them that she wanted to rest for a time.

They left her and went downstairs, but before long a maidservant, who had entered the room to do some small, routine chore, found her mistress was dead.

Lady Huina and her son, Ambrose, returned immediately to the room and removed the ribbon from the corpse's wrist.

There was the mark, distinct and obvious, with the skin withered, and the sinews useless.

Ambrose did, ultimately, marry his cousin, while Lady Huina was given possession of the ribbon and also the diary in which Alistair's ghost had written.

Terrible revenge of 20 dead clansmen

One of the most gruesome crimes for countless years has always been grave-robbing. The ancient Pharaohs went to elaborate lengths to protect their tombs, including the building of the pyramids; in the last century Resurrectionists, of the Burke and Hare type, who did business with the surgeons in selling newly buried bodies were severely dealt with by the authorities, while the modern grave-yard vandals arouse great public hostility.

I mention this because the tale I am about to relate arises from such an act and it was told to me at a ceilidh some years ago.

For many years it has been one of my habits, while touring the Highlands, to tow a caravan and carry a dinghy on top of my car, so I was therefore particularly interested when I heard this tale of spectral vengeance.

Two old army friends, with a driver, set out on such a tour, and during their itinerary came on a suitable camping site near Loch Dubh; the field in which they parked sloped gently down towards the cliff top immediately above the Loch and afforded a panoramic view across its waters to the mountains beyond.

Next day dawned beautifully and the two men rowed across in their boat and began to climb the ridge on the other side.

It was not too difficult an ascent and they were ultimately successful in reaching the summit, just below which they settled down for a time to enjoy the scenery.

The day was particularly calm, yet one of them became aware of a faint, but distinct draught, from the boulders in front of which they reclined, and after removing some of the surface stones, his investigation found that they covered the entrance to a cave.

Moreover, the stream of fresh air that came through strongly suggested that the cave was open ended, so after some further examination, they found that it was a dry, and not too long tunnel, passing right across the mountain ridge, just below the summit, in much the same way as an attic corridor in the roof of a large house.

The other end was also covered by a pile of loose stones and these too were not very difficult to remove, as the larger rocks could be pushed off quite easily and they then began to roll down the hillside, to finally drop into the waters of the Loch.

From this end they could look over the water to where their caravan was sited, but they immediately saw the gesticulating figure of their driver, who was obviously very agitated about something.

They waved back to him, but it took some time for it to dawn on them that the rolling stones had caused a minor avalanche and part of the fall had struck and holed their dinghy, which was moored almost directly below.

It then required some Indian sign language to inform their driver that he would have to contact the Hotel, from where he could hire a boat and obtain the services of a ghillie to ferry them back across the Loch, but, finally, he understood and set off.

While they awaited transport, one of them went down and rested near the water's edge, idly watching the ripples lapping onto the stones, while the other returned to explore the tunnel that they had discovered.

All was quiet for a time, when the one at the Loch's edge heard something rolling down the hillside.

It was white, and shone up clearly in the strong sunlight, contrasting against the dark, carboniferous rock, and it passed quite close to him before plopping into the Loch; it was obvious that it was a human skull.

It was followed shortly afterwards by some other skulls and then, at intervals, came showers of human bones.

What had happened was that the excavator in the tunnel had come on an old graveyard there, possibly used to bury the casualties of some ancient clan war.

In such cases the corpses were occasionally buried upright, shoulder to shoulder, as a mark of honour, as was found when they excavated under the church at the old hillside cemetery of Cillechueril, near Roy Bridge.

Why he should have in any way interfered with them or why he should have cast some out to roll down the hillside is, however, completely unaccountable, unless he wanted some proof of his gruesome discovery.

It was getting on for evening when their relief boat arrived and one of the pair afterwards admitted that he felt decidedly uneasy about his companion's wanton disturbance of the dead.

They were, however, soon back at the caravan and he did not say anymore about the incident as they began to prepare a meal and the driver took the boatman home.

It was late in the gloaming when he returned and he was obviously very disturbed to tell them a curious story of having to pull up on the road to avoid a group of fierce looking kilted men, all armed with sword and shield and obviously preparing for some ambush or sally of battle.

So much so that he had to slow down almost to a halt, and when he looked again, the road was completely deserted with not a soul in sight.

During the night they followed the usual custom of one sleeping in the caravan with the window wide open, with the other in his own little tent, while the driver slept in the car.

The weather was particularly mild and the tent dweller, who was a light sleeper, and who was still a little disturbed by his companion's actions during the day, suddenly became aware that there was movement around the site. He thought he must be mistaken and tried to settle down but there it was again, a fleeting, furtive movement. So, zipping back his sleeping bag, he crawled over to the opening in his tent and peered out.

The darkness was now well dispersed by an almost full moon, but he was absolutely astounded to see more than a score of strong, kilted clansmen, and he received no response when he called several times to his colleague.

It was now very evident that the mysterious visitors were up to some mischief, and by now he was thoroughly alarmed and he shouted for their driver, who must already have been awakened as he came across almost immediately.

Dead clansmen take revenge

They both ran towards the caravan, shouting as they went, but no-one emerged and then they noticed that it was moving, slowly, almost imperceptibly, but definitely moving; yet more strangely still the legs had been raised and it was obvious that the brake had been released, while it quickly began to gather speed down the slope.

They ran helplessly after it and did get near enough to hammer on its rear wall, but there was no response from within.

They had to stand and watch as it projected itself from the top of the cliff, out, and then down, into the waters of the Loch.

Looking around, they saw that they now had the field to themselves, and an eerie stillness with a deep silence seemed to have settled around them.

The driver immediately sped off to the village for help, and the lone camper began to pick his way down towards the water's edge, but, on reaching it, he found it very deep at that part.

Within an hour a large group of volunteers were in action, but even with them it was quite some time before the body was recovered from the van.

Phantoms of mother and baby at Glenfinnan?

The Western Highlands of Scotland have a sad, savage history, but one that is immensely rich in folklore, with many tales of ghosts and hauntings. No doubt this feature has been nurtured through the years by the very fact of their geographical isolation, but has also possibly been developed by the fact that the countryside is of difficult terrain, bringing danger, mystery and uncertainty up to the very walls of the clachan.

There we have high mountain masses, sheathing long stretches of dark loch water, with undulations of bracken-backed moorland, wandering off into a deep wilderness that is ultimately edged by the hard, rock-spurred and treacherous coast, so often assailed by the fierce surges of the wild Atlantic.

Then there are also the heavy scents from the peat fire and the soft lilt of the Gaelic language, forming an ideal setting for the eerie story whispered around the hearth of some remote croft during the blackness of the long Highland night.

My own association with the area is now a long one, as also is my interest in supernormal happenings, so it perhaps is the powerful fusion of two such factors that incites me to recount some incidents from the vast reservoir of stories that may perhaps just give us the merest glimpse behind the veil of the great unknown.

The first situation took place at the little railway station of that historic village, Glenfinnan, situated alongside the famous 'Road to the Isles' at the head of Loch Sheil and the scene where the standard was raised by Bonnie Prince Charlie for the start of the ill-fated 1745 rebellion.

Here, my brother was station master, but like so many weird stories, it still leaves some uncertainty as to whether the eyes, the ears or maybe both have been deceived, or whether there is a simple, natural, but unknown explanation. Perhaps if the person concerned had a more highly developed psychic sense, he may have suspected the presence, or, on the other hand, been able to dismiss the slightest possibility of there being anything unusual.

On the evening of which I write, he was working alone in his office after the last train from Glasgow had passed, this being normal routine for the person on late duty, as that part of the West Highland railway is single line track, except at the stations, which are the only places at which trains can pass. Once a train has left the station, the section is automatically closed as far as signals and points are concerned, until it is cleared from the next station by a contrivance called the 'Tablet System'.

When the last train has gone, the operator must remain on duty until it has passed the adjacent station, which is about ten miles distant, so that he can then prepare the way for the first train down in the morning.

On that particular evening, he was awaiting this bill code from his neighbour and was rounding off his clerical work for the day.

Here, I may add, that from Fort William, both road and rail run for much of the way fairly near to each other, passing closely alongside the northern shore of Loch Eil. The railway then goes over a mighty viaduct, but both skirt the head of Loch Sheil, then, after Glenfinnan village, almost touch the lapping waters of Loch Eilt, allowing the passenger a fleeting glimpse of Loch Ailort and Loch Nan Uamb before reaching the coast.

At the time of which I write there was no other road, and no diversions between Glenfinnan and Arisaig, although since then a picturesque new thoroughfare has been built from Loch Ailort, through Glennig to Kinlochmoidart, while a forestry track as far as Polloch has been constructed on the southern side of Loch Sheil.

Then, there was just one road and the railway, running closely together, and normally flanked on one side by a Loch, and on the other by the bracken covered foot-hills of the mountains.

My brother still remembers that the evening in question was beautiful, with the summer sun setting very low and its rays producing a kaleidoscopic spectrum on the surface of the loch, while the mountains were starkly silhouetted against the reddening sky.

He could just see a well antlered stag wandering through the upper crags of a corrie, while a buzzard winged its heavily laboured flight into the foothills, and a lone fisherman stood in his boat to cast his fly rhythmically over the evening rise on the water.

Otherwise, there was a great stillness and a deep silence, when he suddenly became aware that there was someone on the platform.

This in itself was unusual, because normally, and especially in the quiet of the evening, he would hear anyone come up the wooden stairway, which climbed fairly steeply to the station platform from the road.

The visitor, a woman, was wheeling a child of some months in a pram, and he immediately noticed that she was tall, dignified, strikingly beautiful, and attractively dressed.

Any callers, of course at the country station were few and far between at that time of the day, as the local people were well acquainted with the times of the trains, whereas the shades of evening were now well set in.

In any case, as soon as the lone clerical worker saw them appear, he put away his ledgers and left the office to inquire their business, and, when the lady spoke, it was with a refined and dignified charm, yet her diction revealed no trace of any particular accent.

She told him simply that she was on the way to Mallaig, the terminus of the West Highland railway line, but he was sorry to inform her that she had missed the last train of the day by almost half an hour.

"But I really don't want a train, you see I have no money . . . nor could I even promise to send it to you later . . . I have walked so far . . . Oh! it seems so very far . . . and I must walk the rest of the way".

"With a pram and a baby? It's a long way and the road's pretty hilly and a bit rough in parts", said my brother.

This was at the time of the old road, and anyone who can remember it would agree that this description of it was the understatement of all time.

"I'm sure we'll manage. There's some light left yet and we're fortunate that the weather seems set for a fine night".

"Well, that's maybe true, but it's a lonely countryside and the scene can change quickly, with a long way between the villages, but . . . is there anything I could do to help you?"

"Well, I was thinking that we could possibly shelter here for the night. Perhaps you would allow us to sit in one of the waiting rooms, or even in a storage shed . . . I would be most grateful".

This request was not an unusual one in that district, as the station staff sometimes allowed drenched hikers, climbers or campers to pass a night indoors, so that they could dry out their gear . . . but the station master had never met a situation quite like this.

"Certainly", he answered immediately. "I'll put a fire in the waiting room and my wife will lend you some blankets. Will the baby be alright there?"

"Oh yes, I'm sure he will. He's tired now and he'll sleep in the pram. I really am most grateful to you".

"Will he need anything special? Maybe a little hot milk?"

"You're very kind. The very last thing in the world I want to be is a nuisance . . . but . . . well, if it wouldn't disturb your wife too much, that would be sincerely appreciated".

Meantime, he went along to his house, which was just adjacent to the station and it so happened that his wife had just finished a baking of bannocks, scones and pancakes. She arranged a selection of these on a tray with some butter and jam, made a pot of tea and set aside some warm milk for the baby and then accompanied him back with a pillow, sheets and some blankets. The woman was obviously delighted, while a roaring fire was soon licking the bars of the grate, ignited by some tinder-dry pine logs, fir cones and a liberal sprinkling of paraffin oil. So, having seen to their basic comfort, he lit the lamp, bade them a good night and left her to enjoy her supper.

In the morning he came up very early to the station to find that the few dishes had been washed and dried, the fireplace cleaned out, the

Mother and baby — or ghosts?

sheets and blankets neatly folded, but there was absolutely no sign of the woman and her child.

He thought little of this at the time, assuming that she had decided to set off early, but he had to admit to himself that he felt some peculiar sense of disappointment, because he had already decided to give her the fare to Mallaig.

Later in the day, however, a fish lorry on its way south with a catch from the port called at the station and he asked the driver the whereabouts of a woman on the road with a pram. He was informed that there was absolutely no sign of any pedestrian, with or without a pram, and, as I have already said, there was no alternative route. As the day wore on the situation began to trouble him, so he phoned the neighbouring stations in either direction and also some cottages that were situated along the roadside, but there was absolutely no word of his visitors.

Towards evening, in spite of many enquiries from roadmen and travellers, there wasn't even the slightest trace, so he reported the matter to the police, who made a thorough enquiry from Fort William to Mallaig. But it was just as if they had vanished.

Ultimately, the lochs were dragged, the peat bogs probed, the burn courses investigated and an exhaustive search by experts was initiated, but there was neither sign or trace of any living soul, far less a pram. No other person admitted to ever seeing them, and this in a remote rural area where strangers are very conspicuous.

Dance of the wee folk lasted for 100 years!

In the ancient folklore of Scotland, there are many references to the existence of the fairies, or the Sith, as they are called in the Gaelic, while similar tales also come from Ireland, the Isle of Man and from various parts of England.

The origins of this belief date back into far antiquity. Some hold that at one time the 'Wee Folk' actually existed on earth, but are now extinct, or perhaps just invisible to the normal mortal's eyes; others believe that they are to be found in little hillocks, dancing and feasting during a pleasant evening, and in Ireland it is not uncommon to see a ring, usually of hawthorn trees, take up a fair proportion of the arable land on a croft, yet many farmers would not risk incurring their wrath in ploughing through it, because there are many reports on the misfortunes that usually follow such a rash act.

Among the believers, it is held that they are normally of very small stature, usually dressed in green or grey, but endowed with the power to take up any size or shape that the occasion demands.

Generally speaking, it is also considered that they are not very friendly disposed to the human species, and even to those who have on some account won their friendship, they are thought to be easily offended, capricious and quite mischievous, while, if they are really roused, they can be capable of quite venomous behaviour.

More theologically minded people have a theory that at the instance of Original Justice, when Lucifer and his followers rebelled against the infinite majesty of God, and were, in consequence, expelled from Heaven to Hell, there would be an exterior fringe element, who were obviously not quite so guilty as the inner circle of instigators.

Nevertheless, although they were excluded from the Beatific Vision, they were not cast into the dark recesses of Hell, and it is these creatures that are now known as the fairies.

Those who believe in them tend, to some extent, at least to have a fear of them and consider that it is advisable for you to go out of your way to be friendly towards them, although direct association is neither desirable, or fortunate.

Many of the tales concerning Da Sith introduce the theme of the incompatible connection between time and the infinite and the period of association which some mortal person has with them is not paralleled in any way in our normal hourly sequence. So, when they return from their experience, which has seemed to be of reasonably short duration, they find that a considerable time, often many years, has passed.

The Sith are also believed to possess great musical talent and to have an intense love of dancing. It is, therefore, not surprising that there are places in Sutherland, the Isle of Tiree, Kintyre, Invernesshire and Ross-shire, where some people maintain that they hear the strains of mystic pipes or melodies played on a fairy organ, which is said to have a curious plaintive sound, blending into the weird sighing of the night wind.

In Ireland, there is a traditional belief that the Londonderry Air was first heard by a late evening reveller coming past a place where a fairy gathering was being held.

On hearing this attractive tune, that was unknown to him, and fortunately having the ability to write music, he was able to scribble down the notes of the melody and thence to reproduce it afterwards on an instrument.

One tale that substantiates the suspicion of fairies being easily annoyed or upset, comes from the Isle of Mull, where there was a well known little green hillock that was commonly believed to be a citadel of the Wee Folk.

So long had it been left without the slightest harassment, and so ideally was it situated, that the position was that the Sith had become particularly well disposed towards the local people.

The villagers would leave delicacies and presents out for them, while in the evening, they would also present tasks for them, as apparently they possessed. great ability and had a variety of skills to undertake any type of repair or mending work, varying from fixing a plough share to darning cloth, while they were not unknown to throw in a length of the most beautifully woven cloth.

This too, was usually always done in one night and the repaired articles would be there in the morning to delight the locals.

There was, however, an awkward member of the community who

seemed absolutely determined to find out exactly what they could do, and he kept giving them more and more difficult tasks to perform.

His ultimate request was when he left them a long lath of sea flotsam and asked that it be made into a mast for his boat. This, apparently, was the last straw, and in the morning neither that or anything else was done, while there was not the slightest sign of them for evermore. Where they went no-one knows.

The majority of reports about fairy behaviour usually concern themselves about this strange inequation with human time and this particular one is a traditional tale, involving two wandering fiddlers.

The two bands had wandered into Inverness, in the hope that they would earn some money playing in the taverns and in the streets, but the winter had set in early and there was a hard chill in the air, with snow on the hills, and a biting wind that suggested there was more to follow.

People on the streets were only too keen to return to the warmth of their fireside, and those who had to travel were setting off early on their journeys, and it all meant that there was little notice, far less reward, for the entertainers.

So, ultimately, they made their way across the old oak bridge, which at that time was the only way over the Ness, and they made their way down the riverside.

They had not gone far along this path when they met a strange figure of a man, old, bearded, small and unusually dressed, with a peculiarly strange type of cap, but he appeared to know them both, as he addressed them by name. He asked them if they would accompany him, as he required two fiddlers for a celebration that was about to take place, and the reward would be high, so, needless to say, they agreed to play.

He took them back across the old bridge and then set out towards the Hill of Tomnahurich, about which the Brahan Seer had something to say, and half way up that ascent, he suddenly began to stamp his foot on the turf.

Then they saw a large entrance leading to a brightly lighted and most inviting hall with ornate candelabra, tables laden with food and wine and a laughing, gay, dancing company, all dressed in green.

The visitors were lavishly wined and dined, after which they entertained the company with a wide selection from their repertoire and the night passed with the sound of their music and the merry clatter of the company.

Ultimately, however, the strange old man came back to say that it was now near morning and time for the entertainment to end, so he escorted them towards the exit, giving them a purse of money as their reward.

So generous was the payment, that one of the fiddlers called down the blessing of God on the company, but at this mention, the whole scene disappeared and they found themselves back on the cold, frost-hardened hillside.

Slowly they trudged back to the town, but here they immediately noticed great changes.

The old oaken bridge had gone and had been replaced by a handsome stone edifice, with several arches; the buildings were different and many had disappeared; the people had altered in manner, speech and

The two fiddlers are welcomed
to the fairy dance

dress, so much so, that they were laughed at as they passed.

It was all so peculiar that they made off towards their own village, where they found that their contemporaries had died many years before.

Then they made towards the church and as they entered, the minister was just pronouncing the Blessing and they both crumpled away before the very eyes of the congregation.

The gold that they had in their possession fell to the floor amidst their dust, and it is reckoned that the dance had lasted for nearly a hundred years.

In the rural areas of both Ireland and the Highlands of Scotland there is a fairly widespread fear of the harm that the fairies may do if their mounds, dwellings or rings are in any way disturbed, and rowan trees around the property, a cross of rowan twigs or cold iron in the form of a horseshoe above the door, are frequently used as a protection to the occupants.

I remember being out walking one evening in County Longford, with a gentleman who was Principal of a Technical College, and who now lived in the country.

I asked him about local belief in the existence of the fairies, and his answer was, "Few of them would admit to it if they were asked, but . . ." and we had then come alongside a field with a fairy ring near the middle — "Just look at that; he has only a small croft, yet he's losing quite a lot of land with that ring, but tear it out . . . he wouldn't dream of it".

People, in general, considered it advisable to have good relationships with them. Sir Walter Scott refers to this practice through his famous character, Baillie Nicol Jarvie, in the novel 'Rob Roy'.

One story that I have been told concerning such retribution is a comparatively mild one, but there are many traditional tales, whereby any wanton destruction of their premises is followed by severe misfortune or even death.

This particular incident happened in an isolated part of Sutherland, to a labourer who was sent by his employer to cut peats, and during this work he suddenly became aware of a clear, shrill voice that was scolding him in no uncertain manner, ordering him to replace the turf on the roof of her house.

Looking more closely, he saw the figure of a tiny woman dressed in green, and with long, golden hair down to her shoulders.

As she was so obviously annoyed, he lost no time in replacing the large divot to which she was pointing.

By the time he had completed the repair, the little lady had vanished, but he told his master of the incident and requested that he be sent to work elsewhere on the estate, but he was laughed to scorn.

So he had no alternative but to carry on, and as time passed, he was very surprised that he suffered no misfortune or inconvenience.

Almost a year passed, when he was on his way home one evening, carrying a can of milk for the household, and he passed what was known locally as the Fairy Mound, when, suddenly feeling very tired, he sat down to rest but was soon fast asleep.

When he awoke, the moon was shining brightly and the stars twinkled in the heavens, but he was no longer alone, being surrounded by a laughing, dancing, throng of the Wee Folk.

Then, seizing him by the hands, they pulled him to his feet and forced him to join the revelry, and the rest of the night was passed in this way.

Finally, there was the unmistakable sound of a cock crowing from a nearby farm, and the dancers all rushed towards an entrance in the mound, dragging him with them, but once inside they immediately collapsed in a sort of exhaustion, and were soon fast asleep.

When the labourer awoke, he was dazed and the fair little woman in green came up, touched him on the shoulder, and said: "The grass has now grown over the roof of my dwelling. No great damage was done, so you can now go home, but first you must swear never to speak to anyone of what you have seen here".

He gladly gave this promise, and when he passed through the exit, the can of milk was there from, as he thought, the night before.

It was only when he arrived home that the reality of the situation came to him, as his children had grown greatly, and his wife accused him of desertion. Seven years had apparently elapsed and this was his punishment from the Sith, although comparatively, a very mild censure

Thirteen disciples in the Devil's Dozen!

There has always been a wide general interest in witchcraft, but it is a subject that means very different things to various people, while reference to the cult has claimed the attention of many great authors, poets and dramatists throughout the years.

There are, of course, many facets of the practice, from astrology and storm raising to magic and necromancy, yet although something is known about the paraphernalia and rituals of the cult, its precise origins are lost in the mists of time.

There is always with us the popular nursery image, where the ugly witch is the villain of the fairy tale, the pantomime character, the gruesome hag with her cats, her broomstick and her incantations, all of which are simulated at Hallowe'en.

There is also, however, the historic reality of the fearful persecutions that took place during the late seventeenth and early eighteenth centuries.

During the period of superstitious hysteria, there must have been many unfortunate creatures who were either simple minded, eccentric, insane, peculiar or perhaps just innocent recluses, who were accused and subsequently executed by fire, while others again were denounced out of sheer personal malice and then condemned from the testimony of false witnesses.

Many confessed under the imposition of the most cruel tortures, others were sentenced on the flimsiest of evidence, such as the possession of certain animals, suspicious or weird behaviour, being marked with minute blemishes or scars which were said to be the outward signs of a pact with the devil.

Nevertheless, in spite of all this, the origins still remain obscure and some scholars feel that it comes down from the Stone Age Religion, and others, that it stemmed from the mysterious beliefs of the East but was developed by people who also possessed some malignant wish to mock and parody Christianity.

The basic cell or unit is called a Coven and consists of thirteen members, twelve ordinary and one directing official, who was generally regarded as a devil, or at least as one masquerading as such.

The odd number of the group is reputed to relate, by tradition, to the twelve apostles chosen by Christ, and this fits into the parody of Christianity pattern, while in Scotland, even today, thirteen is often referred to as the Devil's dozen.

The actual dates reserved for the main meetings of the coven are Candlemas Day (February 2), May Eve (April 30), Lammas (August 1) and All Hallows Eve (October 31) — approximately every quarter of the year.

The location was always at some secluded spot, often a churchyard, or some old ecclesiastical property, but sometimes a house, although the chosen venue had usually some tradition of reverence about it, either on account of it being sanctified ground, or perhaps just possessing some atmosphere, aura or the reputation of mysticism. On occasion, more than one coven would be present at the assembly, so the spot would naturally be chosen as a place suitable to accommodate the required number.

The meeting of the coven was held mainly for the conduct of business, but after that much of the time seems to have been taken up by dancing, singing and feasting.

The overall pattern resembles, at least to begin with, the statutory meeting of any other small group or society, in that they are required to produce reports of their activities, take part in discussion, receive advice on procedure and to accept instruction or encouragement for the future.

This was followed, on occasion, by the initiation of new members and by a discussion on the names of those suggested or recommended as suitable recruits.

The actual initiation ceremony was nearly always conducted in a churchyard, or at least on consecrated ground, which again lends weight to its anti-christian nature, and this is certainly true of the cult in its later centuries.

The ritual consisted in the main, of three parts, the first of which was a renunciation of their old faith; then there was a form of baptism, wherein the officiating witch made a cut on the person from which some of their blood was sucked out, spat out on the hand and then sprinkled on the head, after which they were given another name, known as a 'spirit name'; finally they were given a mark which signified that a covenant had been entered into between the witch and the Devil. The new disciples then learned of the services that they were to receive by the use of various charms, incantations and rituals, while the Devil informed them personally of the shape in which he would appear to them.

The most interesting part of the process of initiation was the imprinting of the Devil's mark on the novice, which was done by nipping or branding in some part of the body and in appearance was very like the impression of the foot of a hare or a rat, but it was of such a nature that it would not bleed, even when pierced by a pin or a needle.

The precise spot of the body chosen was often in a hidden place, sometimes under the hair of the head, or the eyebrows, and often in a covered part, such as beneath the eyelids or armpits.

The mark itself was usually withered or brown in colour, and even when deeply pierced by a needle, there was no bleeding and the witch felt no pain.

The finding of such a mark was at one time considered as almost conclusive proof of being a witch and is often confused with the possession of a small tumour or teat from which the familiars or imps are supposed to feed.

After the business side of the meeting there came the more frivolous part of the sabbat, culminating in dancing, usually beginning with a ring dance, which was performed in a circle, and they moved in a direction contrary to the sun's motion and around some object.

This is known in Scotland as Widdershins, and this appears to have been an integral part of Witch routine, certainly in this part of the world, and it was followed by a line dance that was led by the master of ceremonies.

The type and quality of the food provided was usually of a fairly common or normal variety, but at the main meetings there was often a special diet produced and this could be of excellent taste, but it could also be revolting, so much so that it could upset even the most fanatical of the devotees.

The most active period of witch persecution in Scotland took place during the last decade of the sixteenth and the first half of the seventeenth century, (1590 - 1650), there being three separate phases, and even conservative estimates reckon that between 3,500 and 4,500 executions took place during the period 1560 until 1660.

The first complaints were normally made to the Church and the Kirk Session initiated the early investigations, while evidence was solicited from neighbours and from those who had brought about the enquiry.

The accused was imprisoned, often in solitary confinement so that a confession might be obtained, and if this was not forthcoming as a voluntary gesture, then there were a wide variety of excruciating tortures that could be used and these normally brought forth the desired result.

The victim was stripped to the waist and frequently left completely naked, after which the head was shaved and the skin then closely scrutinised from scalp to toe. Any mark or blemish found was pierced to a depth of several inches with a long brass pin and if the person felt no pain and it did not bleed, then the test was regarded as positive.

For a time there was an actual trade of being a witch pricker, with an appropriate period of training beforehand.

Gradually, however, the infallibility of the Witch Mark came under doubt, but any confession that was extorted formed the main case for the prosecution when the person was brought to court.

The ultimate fate of the unfortunate accused was usually to be strangled and then burnt at the stake with the consequent scattering of their ashes, but in addition to that, some fiendish barbarities were also perpetrated against those who persisted in proclaiming their innocence.

The scenes during the actual burning were, of course, gruesome in

*Harsh 'Justice' for an alleged
disciple of Satan*

the extreme, with recorded instances of the half-burned victim breaking free, only to be returned to the flames by the executioners.

The last legal trial in Scotland for witchcraft was in 1727, and in this case, the prisoner, Janet Home, was executed by a means that had, only on occasion, been used previously, namely that of being burned in a barrel of pitch.

There were many forms of the spells, rituals and mysterious ceremonies that have been carried out by witches throughout the ages and in various parts of the world, but one factor that appears to influence many of them is that some object in the person's possession seems to become a sort of focus of a desired effect, as we shall see when we consider the various types of Witch Rites.

1. *Sympathetic Rites:*— This was the simplest and the most common rite, involving the production of a wax image of the victim and then baptising this in his or her name. Pins were either stuck through certain parts of the image or it was allowed to melt before a fire, or again it might be laid in a pool of a stream, and what was done to the little image was wished to be inflicted on the person concerned. When such a curse was centred on the children of a family, the heating would be done more gently and would take place daily, over a period of time, but if one of the children died then the image would be removed and the ritual resumed when another was born.

It is not difficult, however, to imagine that with the great variety of wasting diseases, like cancer, tuberculosis, declines and many others, for which there was no known cure at the time, that the witches would be blamed for much of which they were entirely innocent.

2. *Transference Rites:*— These were mainly used to inflict a disease on someone or to transfer sickness from one person to another, or from a person to an animal.

Many who practice witchcraft, have, of course, a basic medical knowledge, some of which has been handed down through the generations and the rest acquired through study, observation and experience.

I once read an article in a Medical Journal, written by an army doctor who had spent some time treating natives in Africa before the Second World War.

In the region where he worked he experienced great competition from the local witch doctor, to whom the people were strongly attracted and it had to be admitted that some of his treatments were surprisingly successful.

For example, there was one which involved the application of a plaster of green mud, scraped together from the most overgrown and slimiest part of the riverside and this was used to cover the cut or infected part.

It was, of course, the very antithesis of all the basic principles in medical practice, but invariably the cut or infection healed up cleanly.

This was many years before Sir Alexander Fleming experimented with moulds to find out about Penicillin and that treatment had been used for centuries.

3. *Sympathetic Milk Rite:*— There was a common and widespread superstition that witches had the power to take milk from other peoples' cows, even those kept at some distance away from them, and witchcraft was also blamed for the sudden and unaccountable cause of a cow going dry.

Here again there was a recognised ritual involving certain incantations, while the material involvement was a certain type of rope or hair and which, when finally cut, would allow the supply to be r e s t o r e d .

4. *Animal Rites:*— Animals have always been reputed to play an intrinsic part in Witch Rites. The animals concerned are usually cats, but there are also instances of dogs, hares and crows also on occasion being involved.

They may be used as charms, but also as possible mediums for causing disease or bringing harm to people, but sometimes rather to cure disease and for quelling as well as causing storms at sea, a power which was strongly associated with certain witches.

It was also believed that at least some witches had the power to change themselves into certain animals and there is a great abundance of tales in various folklores relating to how such animals would be wounded, and when transformed back to the witch the wound would still be evident.

5. *The Elf Arrow Rite:*— These were said to be used by the black witches as a weapon which could be lethal, but also by the white witches as a protection and cure against the spells and malevolence of the black.

The arrows were small flints and all of them had a certain uniformity of shape, so the popular superstition was they were actually fashioned by the Devil himself, or by the fairies. Again, much of the sickness that was not understood was attributed to the fairy arrows, which were said to fly in the dark.

6. *Evil Eye:*— This belief is one of the most primitive, but also one of the most extensive and there is a phrase for it in most languages, e.g. "Mauvais Oeil" in French, "Boser Blick" in German and "Buidseachd" in the Gaelic, while in some English speaking parts of the world it is also referred to as Fascination.

The basic tenet relates to the power of the eye, and in this case, it is stimulated by a wish for evil happening, together with the hostile look, but it is also accompanied at times by a sort of incantation.

It was thought of as a sort of hierarchy amongst witches. I have come across a form of it in the West Highlands, and in this case, the person was thought to have become possessed of it naturally, and perhaps against their wishes, in a somewhat similar way as to how others have and obtained the Second Sight.

One meaningful, hostile glare from such a person was said to be enough to bring destruction and havoc to either man or beast. A remedy against it recommended by King James I in his work on witchcraft was the common Rowan Tree.

Towards the end of the sixteenth century, witch hysteria broke loose in Aberdeen and in a fairly short period of time there were twenty four burned at the stake, while the charges against them covered almost the whole range of Witch Rites.

One, Janet Wishart, was accused of casting spells, and it was also held that several people had died because of her use of the Evil Eye. She was also charged with storm raising and dismembering a corpse that had been left suspended from a gallows, as there was a belief that witches used the ingredients taken from the bodies of executed criminals to dispense their magic potions and killing ointments.

Then, in 1647, Isobel Gowdie, possibly the best known of the Scottish Witches, made confessions that were apparently not obtained by the use of torture. In these she detailed her whole career as a witch, from her initial pact with Satan, her renunciation of Christianity, her receipt of the Witch Mark and much that involved her in the various Witch Rites.

She, however, also spoke of the Familiars or Imps which are a sort of exclusive feature of British Witchcraft and not much mentioned in the accounts of Continental Witch Trials.

The basic belief here, is that the Devil gives the Witch a low ranking demon in the form of a small domestic animal to serve her, and to do any malevolent mischief for her, while she in return, would succour and nourish it.

Unlike her predecessor, Janet Wishart, who was burned along with another over a fire of peat, tar and coal, there is however, no record of Isobel Gowdie being executed, but it seems extremely likely that only her death itself would let her escape from the vengeance of the flames.

Family cursed by seer they spiked and roasted in tar

One of the most famous and probably the most memorable of the seers in the various parts of the Highlands was Kenneth McKenzie, better known as Coinn Each Odhar, who was said to have been born in the Parish of Nigg, about the beginning of the seventeenth century.

There is inevitably some legend and there are several versions of the way in which he became possessed of the gift of prophecy, but the various stories have the common feature that he was occupied in cutting peats somewhere in the vicinity of Brahan Castle.

This, of course, was a common agricultural task of the time as these were stacked, dried and used for fuel, but during this particular shift, Kenneth felt weary, sat down to rest and fell fast asleep.

On awakening, he found that he was possessed of a stone with a hole in it and by it came the acquisition of super-normal power, with which he was, from then on, greatly endowed.

Within a very short time of finding this, he was able to recognise that the dinner, which was carried to him, had been poisoned by the wife of his master, who had taken a violent dislike to him because of his wit and fluency, which on several occasions she had found too much for her.

There are also some variations in the reports of what was supposed to be the colour of this stone. Some say it was blue and others say white; there are also differences in whether or not there was supposed to be a hole through it.

For myself, I do not believe that the stone was in any way important, but I do feel that Kenneth felt that it was. Realising that he was the recipient of this gift, I think it highly probable that he used the stone as some sort of outward sign to impress people with something material, and to which he could associate some form of his mystical power. Just as conjurers, magicians and impressionists use props, he used the stone, but I feel that it was, to use modern parlance, a gimmick.

What we do know of the character of the Brahan Seer is that he was obviously.a man of great intelligence, possessed a ready wit, and appears to have had a highly developed ability for conversation.

Because of this, there seems little doubt that some of his predictions may have been due to sheer natural wisdom and accurate observations, without having any recourse whatever to supernormal powers.

He did predict that ships with unfurled sails would one day pass and repass Tomnahurich and this hill would be placed under lock and key, while the fairies would be secured within.

This pleasant place had a local reputation as a 'Fairy Hill', but the opening of the Caledonian Canal, some one hundred and fifty years later, fulfilled the first part of the prophecy, and there is now a beautiful cemetery at the top of Tomnahurich, which is surrounded by a fence with a gate and a lock that is secured in late evening and during the night.

It is, of course, very possible that an intelligent man of foresight, in a countryside where there is a veritable profusion of great lochs, may have visualised that in the future there could be some sort of linking between them.

Also, in the case of the Fairy Hill, he, being an agricultural labourer, would probably be familiar with the type of terrain and the situation of ground that would be suitable for a cemetery, and these are very often sectioned off.

Other prophecies which have certainly come to pass refer to the great depopulation of the Highlands and to clansmen moving out before an 'Army of Sheep', and one unusual prediction, which was completely misunderstood at the time, was that fire and water should run in streams, through all the streets and lanes of Inverness.

This, of course, came to pass with the gas and mains water supplies, but again, one would definitely hesitate to attribute it to any supernormal power, just as his statement that two sea banks, some distance from the shore, would ultimately form the coast.

This happened after some considerable time, but again, it may have been the outcome of careful observation of the effect of the tides on the sand banks.

Although it is possible to suggest some natural reasons for the above, the seer did make predictions, some of which did not, or have not yet, come to pass, but he also made a great many that concerned the clan chieftains and other well-known families of the Highlands, while a great number of them actually did happen.

Amongst them was the prophecy concerning the downfall of the great Clanranald of the Isles, who ruled the MacDonalds, both of the Islands and of the mainland, through Keppoch down to Loch Sheilside.

His actual words were — "The old wife with the footless stocking will drive the Lady Clanranald from Nunton House in Benbecula'.

This happened, and the descendants of old Mrs. MacDonald, who used to appear in this not so unusual apparel, occupied the ancient home of the once mighty Chief.

At one time, passing close to the site on which was later to be fought the Battle of Culloden, he exclaimed, "Oh, Drummossie, thy bleak moor shall, ere many generations have passed away, be stained with the best blood of the Highlands. Glad am I that I will not see that day, for it will be a fearful period, heads will be lopped off by the score and no mercy will be shown, or quarter shown on either side".

This, of course, did take place at the last battle to be fought on British soil, where there was a frightful carnage, and from it ensued a long oppression throughout the glens of the north.

Later again, when he was passing the primitive old mill at Millburn, on his way from Inverness to Petty, he foresaw the aftermath of Culloden and the ravages of Cumberland's men, and he proclaimed, "The day will come when the wheel shall be turned for three successive days by water red with human blood; for on thy banks a fierce battle shall be fought, at which much blood will be spilt".

By far the most outstanding episode in the career of the Brahan Seer was, however, his prediction concerning the then powerful family of Seaforth, an incident which brought about his own death. The third Earl of Seaforth had gone to Paris on business, leaving his wife the Countess at their home in Brahan Castle.

The visit, however, which was supposed to be a short one, became protracted, and he indulged in a lengthy stay, enjoying the many pleasures of the French capital.

Ultimately, his lady became restless, then anxious, perhaps suspicious, so she had recourse to the local prophet as time went on and there was no word of his return.

The Seer was duly summoned to the Castle and instructed to give her information about the absent Earl, and after applying the stone to his eye, he was immediately able to tell her that her husband was fit and well, enjoying himself to the full and in good spirits, but not content with this, she became more incisive and probed more deeply, demanding to be told in detail what actually he was doing, and whose company he was in; if his thoughts were centred on her and if he was considering a return home in the near future.

After a period of parrying, and an undoubted show of unwillingness, he must have given her some impression that her husband's occupations were somewhat frivolous, because she began to use the most pathetic entreaties, and even offered him bribes to tell her more.

She demanded a minute account of the Earl's behaviour and a detailed description of his current companions, and the more he warned her that such information would not necessarily make her happy, the more she insisted on receiving it, as she was becoming obsessed by suspicion, jealousy and wounded pride.

She was angered by the seer's disclosures

Ultimately, he relented, and allowed her into the rather sordid scene, whereby the husband was enjoying himself to the full with little, if any, thought of her, their home or their children.

His companions at that moment were the ladies of the court and they cavorted in the grand halls, dressed in fine clothes, indulging themselves with the choicest foods and wines of Gaul.

This, however, brought the age-old response to those who are unfortunate, or foolish enough, to become involved in dispute between husband and wife.

The revelation did not bring gratitude, but a surge of spiteful anger, a stream of venom and vicious vituperation, and all directed at the only available target, namely the man who had brought these devastating tidings to her notice.

Worse still for this powerful and unfortunate woman, was the fact that the final disclosures had been made in the presence of her servants, advisers and closest retainers, so well did she know that her husband's desertion of her would soon be common knowledge in all the great houses of all Scotland.

In her disordered state of mind, she became determined to denigrate the Seer, and denounce him as a felon, who had slandered her good husband's honour, so, having the absolute power of a feudal lord over a serf, she sentenced him to death.

Moreover, little time was to be allowed before the execution, and at first the Brahan Seer did not appear to treat the matter very seriously, but when it became evident that not only was his situation very grave, and his death imminent, as no mercy could be expected from her, he made the following prediction.

"I see into the far future, and I read the doom of the race of my oppressor. The long descended line of Seaforth will, ere many generations have passed, end in extinction and sorrow.

I see a chief, the last of his house, both deaf and dumb. He will be the father of four fair sons, all of whom he will follow to the tomb.

He will live careworn and die mourning, knowing that the honours of his line are to be extinguished forever, and that no future chief of the MacKenzies shall rule at Brahan or in Kintail.

After lamenting over the last and most promising of his sons, he himself shall sink into the grave and the remnant of his possessions shall be inherited by a white-hooded lassie from the east and she is to kill her sister.

As a sign by which it may be known that these things are coming to pass, there shall be four great lairds in the days of the last deaf and dumb Seaforth — Gairloch, Chisholm, Grant and Raasey — one of whom shall be buck-toothed, another hare-lipped, another half-witted and the fourth a stammerer.

Chiefs distinguished by these personal marks shall be allies and neighbours of the last Seaforth; and when he looks around him and sees them, he may know that his sons are doomed to death and his broad lands shall pass away to the stranger and that his race shall come to an end".

In spite of that, Lady Seaforth had him bound and carried to the Ness of Chanonry, where he was unceremoniously thrown head-first into a barrel of burning tar, the inside of which was peppered with long sharp spikes, driven in from the outside. The great irony of the execution, however, was that on the very same day Lord Seaforth arrived home from the Continent.

On hearing of his wife's inhuman sentence, he rode hard, without food or water, in the direction of Chanonry, and it is said that one horse dropped dead beneath him, but nevertheless, he failed to stop it and arrived as the pyre was burning down to its ashes.

He then returned to live with his vindictive wife and ruled for a time before dying in 1678, when he was succeeded by his son.

The family suffered after participation in the 1715 rebellion, but had their estates restored sometime afterwards, so it was not until the latter part of the eighteenth century that the Seer's curse began to be fulfilled.

The last of the Seaforths appeared to have been a man of some ability, and not unpopular, as we read that he raised a regiment, and also held some important posts as Governor in various lands abroad, so this pays great tribute to his personal talents as he was afflicted. He was born in full possession of all his senses before becoming deaf and dumb following an attack of Scarlet Fever. Following this, he could actually speak a little, but became completely inarticulate during the last years of his life.

Those around him were acquainted with the Seer's prophecy, and they well knew that their Earl was the last, because, apart from his disability, he had four sons.

The last of these died very young, but one after the other, the other three sons were taken away.

The last of them had high abilities and was the most promising, but he suffered a long, lingering illness, although there were times when it was thought by some that he would recover.

The old retainer, however, knew that he would go to the grave before his father, and he did.

Sir Bernard Burke, to whom we are indebted for the above version of the prophecies, also writes: "With regard to the four Highland lairds, who were to be buck-toothed, hare-lipped, half-witted and a stammerer, they were marked by these distinguishing personal peculiarities, and all four were contemporaries of the last of the Seaforths.

At length, in 1815, the last of the Seaforths died, having outlived his sons, and the modern title became extinct".

The estates were inherited by his eldest surviving daughter, who was the widow of the famous sailor, Admiral Sir Samuel Hood, and was, therefore, a white-hooded lassie, which was the dress of the time for a young widow.

Shortly after inheriting, she and her younger sister were driving in a carriage in the grounds around Brahan Castle, when the ponies took fright and bolted, so that the conveyance overturned and the sisters were thrown out. From the injuries received, the younger sister died, so that all the tenets of the Seer's prophecies were carried out to the letter. It has been said, however, that the slow, but seemingly inevitable development of these affairs, was observed by many, with much grief and sympathy.

The whole prolonged saga made up one of the most remarkable instances of Second Sight, in a land where these were many.

Tit-for-tat fate of three who shot the Virgin Mary

One of the many very interesting places in the Western Highlands is the small island at the western or seaward end of Loch Shiel, locally known as 'The Green Isle', but originally as Eilean Fhionnon, after St. Finnan, who came to the area from Iona following the death of St. Columba.

Today, the Island can be approached by the short water trip from the Moidart end, but also by a sixteen mile journey from the head of the Loch at Glenfinnan, from where in summer a launch sails daily to Acharache, passing amidst scenery of almost breathtaking beauty.

That was my route of access and as the launch could not berth at the Green Isle, I asked if I could tow my own little boat behind it, to be dropped at Polloch Pier, and from where I could easily row across to the Island.

We berthed the dinghy on the shingle and, on climbing through the undergrowth, we soon reached the ruins of a church that is said to have been built by one of the Clan Ranald chiefs, and there it stood, gaunt roofless and open to the elements, with nettles growing high within its crumbling walls, but still with its altar of rough stone in the place against one of the gables.

The area on the hillside around the church is now a cemetery for the people of the Kinlochmoidart district, with the plots very near to each other and now nearly filled, but in its time the Green Isle has been a penitential place and a centre for pilgrimage for the inhabitants on both sides of Loch Shiel, and this used to take place on the feast of St. Finnan.

Overall, the spot has a long, hallowed history since the missionaries from Iona took up residence there right up until about the twelfth century.

In a niche in the wall behind the altar there is a bell about eight inches high, narrow and tapering towards the top, and it has been exposed there for many centuries.

An interesting story is told about it, so that there are few, if any, local folk who would even touch it.

For a long time it has remained there on that lonely island, neither watched nor guarded, as it is believed that once a party of soldiers on their way from Castle Tioram to Fort William, landed there and took it away, in spite of the legend that all sort of calamities would befall anyone who stole it.

In their case, it is said that they had not travelled far when they could not stop it ringing, whether continuously or spasmodically, I do not know, but they were pursued and overtaken at Glenfinnan, with the result that their leader was severely flogged.

The bell was reinstated to its position, but the tongue was removed, and there it remains, in a niche on the wall of a ruined church on an island overlooking a lovely loch.

When I and my two friends arrived back in our dinghy at Polloch Pier to await the launch on its return journey from Acharache to Glenfinnan, we noticed that there were quite a few aboard compared with the morning journey.

The captain, who had viewed us with some interest on the first trip, took an early opportunity to make his way through the throng on the small deck and speak to us.

Following a few initial pleasantries about the weather or some other trivialities, he then came brusquely to the crux of his concern, and asked: "You didn't touch anything on that island, did you?"

"No", said I, "we did not. I too, have heard all about that bell, and I just wouldn't dare".

He nodded his head in agreement and there was a look of content, or perhaps it was relief, as he made his way back to the wheelhouse.

★　　★　　★　　★　　★

The priest who told the following story of the First World War was old, and had been a member of his order for many years.

It concerned three young infantry officers of a Scots Regiment; men typical of their time, harum-scarum, battle-hardened, mentally drugged by the blood and carnage of Flanders. During a respite in the fighting, their units were rested and they were allowed back to base for a few days, and one evening they visited the nearest village where they drank more than their fill.

On their way back to the billet, they came on a wayside shrine of the Madonna, which is not uncommon on Belgian roadsides, and they decided to fire at it.

After some shots with their revolvers one had knocked off a foot; the second ultimately shattered it but the third had only managed to clip off the raised finger.

The following evening, however, all that nonsense was soon forgotten as they were ordered back to their firing line, and the days that followed saw a particularly savage period of combat.

During these exchanges, each received exactly what he had done to the shrine; one was killed by a shellburst, another lost a leg below the knee and the third had a finger shot away.

"Don't you find that an amazing coincidence?", the old priest asked, and we had to admit that we did.

Then he held out his hand and added, "It was me who shot off the finger".

Certainly, he had only four fingers on the hand.

★　　★　　★　　★　　★

Soldiers who shot at the Madonna

The Island of Iona could be called the cradle of Christianity in Scotland, as it was the location of St. Columba's monastery, and the base of operations for his monks in their work of evangelisation on the mainland.

In addition to that, it is the burial place of many Irish and Scottish Kings, while it has been the scene of a large number of ghostly hauntings, both in sound and by sight.

The most common spectres are, not surprisingly, the figures of monks, nearly always garbed in their rough, brown habits, with a girdle of crude cord, but there is little, if any, record of them speaking or engaging in any form of communication.

Apart from their confined life of austere monastic discipline on that exposed and gale swept Island, they also suffered much during the years from marauders.

In the earlier centuries these were mainly of Viking origin, but during the post Reformation hysteria, even the crosses of the graves were cast into the sea, and it is just possible that, in some cases, the bones too were disturbed.

They were sometimes seen in procession, but usually the spectral figure is alone, although ghostly music is sometimes heard, and mysterious lights unaccountably twinkle in various uninhabited parts of the Island.

Some visitors have also reported as having experienced the power of an invisible presence, even to the extent of it preventing their movement in a particular direction.

★　　★　　★　　★　　★

Another form of vision is the re-enactment of a Viking raid.

Several observers, and at different times, have witnessed the longboats making towards the North shore of the Island.

They have seen the rhythmic sweep of the great oars, the emblems clearly outstanding on the billowing sails, the array of shields along the sides, sparkling in the sun, and the fierce faces of the bearded, winged-helmeted men, as they brandish their swords in the challenge.

The groundings of the craft, the invasion, the slaughter of the monks, the looting, the fire-raising and cattle stealing are all clearly evident, as is the departure of the boats, when the region around the White Sands then assumes an unearthly calm as the sea relentlessly sweeps onto the strand.

One observer, who was an artist, was able to draw from memory, the gory scenes, the weapons used and the shape of the ships with the design of the emblems on the sails, and after expert scrutiny, they were said to be appropriate to the tenth century.

History records that there were many forays, but one major assault took place in 986 A.D., when the Abbot and many of the community perished, while the monastery was desecrated and burned.

Foxes that foretell death, Screeching phantom dogs and other strange things

In the western part of Lochaber, I know of two families who are reputed to be 'followed by the foxes'.

This means that when the head of the family is about to die, foxes come from far and near and, when doing so, they have a tameness that is far from their usual nature.

In fact, one elderly shepherd told me that, when visiting such a family during a bereavement, he had literally to step between them, as if they were a large pack of farm dogs.

These beasts are real, live foxes, but they come around the scene of the death like some assembly of mystic pallbearers.

★　　★　　★　　★　　★

Cats are regarded by many as being animals that are particularly sensitive to any form of psychical disturbance, while they also have the reputation of being one of the most common familiars in the history of Witchcraft.

In spite of that, the stories in folklore about their apparitions seem to be fewer than those involving horses, dogs or even rabbits.

One such tale comes from the area around Arisaig, on the coast of Invernesshire, where a phantom dog is said to roam about the foot hills and copses of the area.

It is a large, shaggy collie with staring blood-shot eyes, and its appearances usually take place just before nightfall, so it is known as 'An Cu Glas' or 'The Grey Dog'.

The reason behind this haunting is said to date back to a period when there were severe losses amongst the sheep, and the shepherds were unable to find the cause.

One day, a crofter's wife left her baby in a cradle outside the cottage and went off to fetch water, leaving this collie dog on the premises, but on her return, the cradle was empty and the remains of the savaged baby were scattered grotesquely around the cot.

On his return, the husband appears to have gone berserk and beat the dog savagely to death, after which he cruelly destroyed her litter of pups.

On the very next day it was discovered that the dog was completely innocent and a wild cat was the attacking marauder.

The phantom is reputed to be that collie, exhibiting its displeasure on irascible, unbalanced man.

★　　★　　★　　★　　★

In Selkirkshire, one Laird of Buckholm was generally regarded as an autocratic, violent man who had acquired the reputation of being capable of cruel, blood-thirsty acts. He had a bitter hatred against the Covenanters, so that many of his most fearful atrocities were perpetrated against them.

One such episode involved a father and his son, who had been arrested by the authorities, and for convenience, were imprisoned in the dungeon of Buckholm Tower.

During the night, the drunken, half-crazed owner took it upon himself to execute the two, and this he did, in a barbarous, blood-curdling manner.

For this he was cursed by the man's widow and the boy's mother, who had arrived to visit them, only to find their bodies grimly impaled.

Her wish was that, his evil memories would haunt him forever, like the hounds of hell.

Years later, on the anniversary of this Laird's death many local people say that there is the sound of a pack of baying hounds, and a man's voice calling frantically for help, as if being closely pursued. This continues until the ghostly fugitive reaches the very portal of Buckholm Tower, beats imploringly upon it and begs admittance, but when the door is opened, the clamour ceases and the yard is empty.

★　　★　　★　　★　　★

There are also many hauntings that involve the apparition of horses, but of course, they formed the main mode of transport for centuries of time. Ballachulish House, in Argyllshire, is said to be haunted by the ghost of Stewart of Appin, who gallops noisily up to the threshold and dismounts, before vanishing. The area to the south of Penicuik in Midlothian is also haunted by a galloping horseman, who disappears in the direction of Peebles.

★　　★　　★　　★　　★

I have heard several tales around the Highlands on much the same theme as Sir J. M. Barrie used in his famous play 'Mary Rose', whereby a person goes missing for a period of time due to some mystic intervention.

This is one such instance and concerns a shepherd, Thomas M., who was tending his flock on the hillside one day when a woman, and it was said that she was the most beautiful creature that he had ever seen, rode up to him from the loch-side.

She was mounted on a milk-white stallion of highly pedigreed stock, whose various accoutrements were richly embellished, while there was an exquisite leather saddle, pure silver mountings, an ornately embroidered backcloth, a bridle of delicately interwoven silk threads and shining stirrup of precious metal.

As she drew up the great horse reared and she smiled down at him in

*Thomas meets the beautiful lady
on a milk white stallion*

a slightly inquisitive, but yet, not unfriendly manner, so that he held the reins as she dismounted, thinking her to be some fine lady now visiting the laird at the Big House.

"I'm at a loss to know who you are Ma'am", said Thomas, touching his cap respectfully and he was astonished when she just smiled back at him and told him, quite candidly, who she was and how much power she had, while going on to tell him of certain other hidden and some very secret things.

He was somewhat entranced by her exquisite beauty, and hung on every word that she uttered, so that when she prepared to go, and offered him her lip to kiss, he responded most affectionately.

"Now, Thomas", said she, "having kissed me, my spell lies upon you and my wish is that you accompany me to my own land that stretches far over mountain, moor and sea, while you will remain there for all of seven years."

He then disappeared from the district and it is said that he went off with her and it is also believed that she gave him many gifts . . . the greatest of which was prophecy.

One day, however, he awakened to find that he had been sleeping on the hllside and lying at the exact spot where he met her, and although it seemed just like a few moments before, seven years had passed.

Down in the glen there were now strangers in his house, because after his sudden and unexplained disappearance, the laird had re-let his croft, as Thomas was a bachelor and had no near relatives.

It is said that he remained for some time in the area, sometimes working on the farms, playing at the ceilidhs of the district, often calling at the hostelries, while always astonishing everyone with his prophecies and his playing of the pipes.

He had been known to foretell death or good fortune; he would advise the crofters, on their way to market, telling them what to buy and what to sell; he could pick out a thief and he could tell the lassies whom and when they would marry, and the number of children that they would one day have.

But . . . it was obvious that he was not really happy within himself as he piped his airs, many of which had never been heard before in those parts, but sad or gay, those who once heard them never forgot them, as the general belief was that one day he was pledged to return to the Lady on the milk-white stallion, whenever she would call him, and there is little doubt that she certainly did.

One evening, when he was refreshing himself in a room at the Inn, interesting some with his talk and entertaining all with his music, someone came dashing in to say that a hart and hind had come down from the mountains and into the village street.

They were now slowly walking along the main thoroughfare, towards that place. Thomas, on hearing this, immediately leapt from his seat, left the company and ran out into the street.

There he waited until the hart and the hind came up to him and they parted slightly so that he was able to walk between them. This he did, and the trio passed off from the village towards the foothills of the mountains and all who saw it stood around, silent and still, not even moving until the mystic entourage had disappeared completely from sight.

The fact remained that Thomas was never seen again, but many of his prophecies were remembered, and ultimately came to pass, while some of those who had heard him pipe a reel, a hornpipe, a strathspey or a lament, swore that never before, or since, did they hear the equal of it.

Invisible ghosts knock three times for death

There are many instances recorded about warnings which some people, families or occasionally even fairly large groups receive when they, or someone near and dear to them, are in imminent danger.

In Ireland mainly, but also in some parts of the Western Highlands, there is a belief in the Banshee which is said to follow certain families.

When one of their relations is close to death then the high-pitched shrieking of that entity will be heard, even though the person concerned may be on another continent.

The Banshee is very rarely seen and tradition has it as female, while the families who come under its attention are said to be of pure blooded lineage.

The sounds that are emitted have been described by listeners as shrieking, long drawn out wailing, and mournful howling, while the source of it appears to move around the perimeter of a field, or dodge about between the knolls, rocks or houses on the surrounding terrain.

A more common form of death warning, however, especially in the Highlands is a loud knocking at the door, although sometimes there are just three strong raps, and this even when the house is situated in an isolated place, but when investigation is made, there is no-one there.

In many cases of reputed haunting there are no visible manifestations whatsoever, but distinct audible happenings, with nearly always no apparent attempt at communication.

There are many tales about ghostly telephone calls, the unaccountable ringing of bells, the sound of footsteps or hooves and the mysterious opening and closing of doors.

Very recently I heard a story from a nun who had just returned to Scotland after mission service in Africa.

One evening, just before bedtime, she was sitting reading when suddenly the noise of a motor cycle seemed to come from nowhere and start to drum itself into her head.

This was very unusual in that particular place but the volume of the noise kept increasing, and finally ended with a loud crash.

They were situated in an isolated spot and no visitor was expected, but the sound had been so intense and demanding that she felt compelled to investigate.

After rousing one of her colleagues, she took the station-wagon and set out along the trail, but they had travelled through the bush for over five miles before they came on a motor cyclist who had skidded off the road and crashed into a tree.

He was coming to their station but was completely unexpected, while the noise of his machine could not possibly have been heard from that place, yet without the immediate aid that they administered, he would undoubtedly have died before morning.

These types of situations are of course, exceedingly difficult to pronounce upon, or to refute, especially as certain sounds can be produced in so many different ways.

Various notes can arise from the resonance of wind in the trees, in a chimney or in the eaves of a house; they can be produced by the expansion or contraction of pipes and wires due to a temperature change, or from the effect of dampness and dryness in certain types of wood; in a house they could also come from the rustling of vermin in the wainscot, or birds in the chimneys.

Nevertheless, there are many instances which persist over a long period of time and are heard by a large variety of people in different sets of circumstances, whilst some defy the rigours of a most thorough scientific investigation.

★　　★　　★　　★　　★

A certain house in Edinburgh has now been incorporated into the University complex, but at one time it was the site of a medical school.

It was then owned by a surgeon, who almost certainly would have had dealings with body snatchers and was reputed to have had transactions with the notorious Burke and Hare.

These two were originally resurrectionists, but gradually this became more and more difficult as the relatives of deceased people began to organise themselves into watch parties for a period of at least three weeks following a burial, and the authorities built guard towers, many of which still stand, at some vantage point actually in, or around the cemetery.

The infamous pair then resorted to murder, enticing their victims, who were usually itinerants or street-walkers to their lodging house. There, after saturating them with drink, they would strangle them and take the corpses to the medical school, usually during the hours of darkness, on the same night.

This particular house had the reputation of being haunted but nothing was ever seen although many people said that they heard the shuffling of footsteps near the entrance or on the stairs, as if something was being drawn across the floor.

During the Second World War it was used at times by the Officers' Air Training Corps, and one of my colleagues, who afterwards served right through the hostilities as a pilot in the R.A.F., spent a short time in it.

He is far from being a nervous or over-imaginative type, but he is adamant that he heard the shuffling and fumbling during the early hours of the morning and spent a most disturbed night in the place.

★　　★　　★　　★　　★

On the sea front at North Berwick, there have been reports over a long period of years, about the sound of distant singing, sometimes in the middle of the night, and coming from the direction of the Bass Rock.

The choir is composed of many voices and the arrangement is an ancient version of one of the Psalms.

This has been heard from the days much before those of Marconi and on nights when the Firth of Forth is free of wind, with the sea birds long gone to roost. Tradition has it that this mysterious singing dates back to the time of the Covenanters in the seventeenth century, who were imprisoned on the Rock, and their rendering of the Psalms was then heard over the water on the mainland.

Another similar tale of this mystical recording comes from a house that was sited on the foundations of an ancient priory. One of the family wrote of an antique table around which the children used to gather in the evening and occasionally they could just hear the monastic rendering of the evening hymn, Salve Regina.

★   ★   ★   ★   ★

The following tale concerns a house on the shores of Loch Ness and not very far from Inverness, and here too, there is no recorded instance of any visible entity, although there is much evidence of unaccountable sounds being heard, in the form of female screaming.

One family, who took a lease of the property, sensed some peculiar eeriness about the place almost immediately, so much so that one of the ladies in the party did not wish to stay, but the longer they did remain, the greater became the sense of uneasiness.

In the village too, they soon became aware that locals were observing them closely, and with much curiosity, with an attitude of waiting to hear something unusual. Their questions, too, were carefully inquisitive.

"How do you like living there?"

"Isn't there a queer feeling about that place?"

"Do you sleep well?"

"Some have complained about noises . . . probably animals in the woods, of course."

Nothing unusual occurred until they had been there for almost a week when they were all awakened in the middle of the night by a series of the most piercing screams, female, shrill, penetrating and carrying all the tremulous tensions of extreme terror, but there was no natural explanation of them as they searched the place from top to bottom. The cries did not last long, but echoed stark, cruel tragedy in their every tone and they occurred on two more occasions during their stay.

Before they left, however, they decided to confide in the village people and found that they were not the first occupants to have been disturbed in this way. The local story was that the house had been used by some Highland chieftains just going to make their last stance up at Culloden. While they were making their arrangements one night, they heard a noise in a cupboard and, on investigation, found a young woman there listening to them. In spite of her screams for mercy, they put her to death.

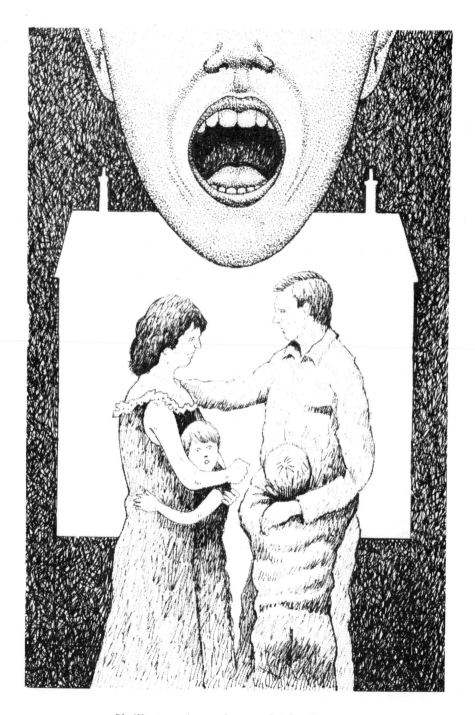

Shrill screaming wakes up the family

Maybe this was the explanation, but that family did not renew their lease the next year, or on any other year.

But where do sound waves go? Do they just diffuse themselves wantonly into space? Is there perhaps some natural method of the recording and reproduction of such waves that is completely unknown to us? Or do very intensely emotional situations, where there has been passion, terror, murder, villainy or imminent danger perpetuate themselves in some unknown way, and are re-enacted on occasion throughout the year?

Kelpies, loch mysteries, and a sea monster with 30 ft. neck

Much has been written about one particular inhabitant of Highland Waters, namely the denizen(s) of Loch Ness, as its sightings number several hundred, but I must say right away that I do not consider that there is anything paranormal about this creature, or family of creatures.

The Rev. J. J. Carruth, monk of the Benedictine Community of Fort Augustus, wrote a very interesting pamphlet in 1954, entitled 'Loch Ness and its Monster', and points out that, apart from the legions of people who have seen this beast, there is an old tradition going back to the time of St. Columba, and probably even earlier, concerning the great creatures which inhabit the Loch and its adjoining river.

St. Adamnan was an Abbot of Iona around 565 A.D. and wrote a biography of St. Columba, in which he mentions 'of the driving away of a certain water monster, by virtue of the prayer of the holy man'.

He goes on to describe the incident, whereby the Saint and the power of prayer, saved a man from death when he was attacked by a great creature, but irrespective of the accuracy of the account, it does show that a belief in the existence was accepted even at that time.

Amongst the people who claim to have seen the monster are many monks of the Abbey and also many people who are very familiar with the waters of the Loch, people who would not normally be deceived by tree trunks or floating debris, while they themselves gained nothing from the experience, merely reporting what they honestly believed they had seen and leaving it at that.

One personal friend of mine, who lived for many years on the side of the Loch, and is now a hotelier further West, in Lochaber, is certain that he saw it on no less than five occasions.

The general description of the creature varies very greatly in respect of its colour, number of humps, speed of travel, length of neck, shape of head and type of wake, but only one or two people make claim to have seen it out of the water.

On the whole, sightings have been more frequent in calm rather than in rough water, in summer rather than in winter, and most of them have been somewhat nearer to the head of the Loch than at the other end.

The Rev. J. J. Carruth also suggests that the creatures are native and have been there for many centuries of time, living mostly in caves, the entrances of which are under the surface of the water and which extend for great distances into the surrounding hills.

This agrees, in general, with many of the findings of more recent explorations and with the belief that the creatures are mammals, who are only seen when they come into the water and rise to the surface to breathe, although they could also possibly remain submerged for long periods and absorb oxygen in much the same way as a frog or sea serpent.

It is interesting to note that Loch Ness (745 ft. max.), is only exceeded in depth by Loch Morar (1,017 ft. max.), which is the deepest Loch in Western Europe, and although it is at a relatively high altitude, the surroundings of Loch Ness are noted for their remarkable mildness, so much so that the snow does not lie unmelted for long on its shores, while ice rarely forms on the surface of its waters.

The old Gaelic writings, however, speak not only of the large beasts in Loch Ness, but also of those in Loch Morar and Loch Sheil.

I am acquainted with two men who claim adamantly to have seen 'Morag', and their reports agree that it is of considerable size.

I am personally more familiar with Loch Sheil, but I can find no description, nor have I heard of any sighting of any large creature during the last seventy years.

It must be remembered though, that the Fort Augustus - Inverness trunk road runs along the western banks of Loch Ness while there is also considerable traffic on the other side, but there is very little on the Northern shores of Loch Morar and practically none along the Southern banks. There is even less around any part of Loch Sheil, so of course, the probability of a sighting becomes infinitely smaller.

★   ★   ★   ★   ★

From both the islands and from the salt water lochs on the West Coast of the mainland, there are a number of observers who describe a long-necked sea monster and these reports come mainly from fishermen and from others with a long experience of the sea. They talk of a creature that rises suddenly from the salt water to a height of from twenty to thirty feet, a long tapering column that sways from side to side as it travels along at a speed of between five and ten knots.

Some mention a small head that turns about and others describe the water swirling above what seems a very large dark mass submerged in the deep.

The creature descends as it arose, leaving a heavy swell of water in its wake, and the descriptions do not vary greatly except in the dimensions that are quoted, but they describe no animal known to marine biologists.

★   ★   ★   ★   ★

The monster rises from the deep

Many of the old Gaelic writings refer to the water horse or kelpie. This entity was considered to be essentially diabolic, and completely in the service of the devil, as it devoted its existence and its energies to the interests of the powers of evil.

It was amphibious in character, attractive in appearance and generally to be found near water, very often in the vicinity of a public thoroughfare, with a loch or pond nearby.

Its mission was simply the destruction of human beings, often without giving them any time to make their peace with God, and thereby claiming their soul for the devil, while the kelpie took possession of their body.

It was, however, generally believed that a kelpie had no basic authority over a human being, unless they themselves agreed to approach, consort with, mount or even molest it, and this of course, shapes the pattern of most forms of diabolic interference.

The technique used by the kelpie lent.itself to attraction, necessity and then deception.

A favourite subterfuge was for it to take the image of a handsome riding horse, with a comfortable saddle and valuable trappings, while it would appear to be completely docile as it grazed naturally at the side of the road on which the weary-traveller would be trudging.

The creature would maintain its pose of being very gentle and calm, until the victim was securely astride and firmly settled in the saddle, when it would give vent to a screeching neigh, like from some sort of fiend that it was, and it would set off at breakneck speed in the direction of the water.

One account of kelpie seduction is said to have happened on Beltane Eve, near Loch Buie on the Isle of Mull.

In this case, a beautiful young village girl was attracted by the appearance and dancing ability of a handsome young stranger, preferring his attentions to that of the local gallants with whom she was familiar.

She allowed herself to be accompanied over the moor towards the shore, before either the peculiarity of his remarks or perhaps some sixth sense, warned her that she was in the company of the notorious Kelpie of Corrywreckan, who was reputed to be able to assume human form at will.

Too late, however, because they were now very near to the water, and seizing her in his arms, he plunged into the sea and was soon dragging her down into the depths, with no one near to answer her terrified cries.

Next morning her drowned corpse was washed up on the shore and legend has it that on Beltane Eve the Kelpie repeats his triumph, as he gallops over the wave tops, with the ghost of the maiden on the saddle before him, and the shrieks of the fiend intermingle with the terrified screams of the girl, like the call of the sea mew on the biting, winter wind.

★ ★ ★ ★ ★

One animal that was, and is held, in great regard by many people of the Highlands and Islands, is the seal.

It had a much higher status than other animals, and was believed to have some obscure, mystical relationship with mankind, while some held that, on occasion, these creatures could assume human form.

Not surprisingly, it was always considered very unlucky to kill a seal, and there are many tales in folklore concerning the misfortunes that ultimately befell someone who committed such an act.

Seals, of course, have a common habit of raising their body out of the water in a vertical stance, so that about half of their length is visible, while they often emit a sort of mewing call, that has an eerie, haunting sound.

In Caithness, the seals were said to be 'Fallen Angels', while there is a group in North Uist who were termed 'MacCodrums of the Seals' and these people were supposed to be the descendants of enchanted seals.

Phantom haunted by a confession . . .

The great majority of hauntings have no known purpose, although there is often an attempt to associate some with an act of extreme violence, but there are a few where the spectre appears to be looking for, or attempting to do something, that was perhaps left undone.

The shades of royalty and autocratic nobles have been seen wandering about certain rooms in their castles, the ghosts of clergymen haunting their churches and the spirits of parents coming to their children in time of need.

One strange instance was experienced by a priest, Father M . . ., who was then a curate in the Archdiocese of St. Andrews and Edinburgh.

Not long after his arrival at a parish in Fife, he was summoned one night to a sick call at a house in the country and in a district with which he was not yet familiar.

He immediately cycled off in the direction of the place, as that was the young clergyman's mode of transport in those days and when he came near to what he thought must be the approximate location of the house, he saw a child standing in the middle of the road and indicating the way up to a particular cottage.

"Up there, Father. You're required at that house".

On entering the house, he found an elderly woman, alone, bed-ridden and apparently very ill, but there was no one else about.

He gave her all the spiritual comfort that he could and made arrangements to immediately call the doctor and a nurse, and although she was overjoyed and much relieved, she persisted in asking how he came to know about her.

"Didn't you send for me?"

"No, how could I. There was no one here to send, and when I took this turn I could not leave my bed."

"Is this not . . .?" He mentioned the address to which he had been called.

"No, no. That's fully half a mile further on".

"But the child? Who . . .?"

"There's no child here now Father".

Still puzzled, he summoned medical assistance for the old lady and made his way to the other address, where he had to attend to a sick man, but on the following morning, as early as he possibly could, he made his way back to the lonely old lady to see if he could be of any further assistance.

When he arrived there, he found that she had died just an hour or two previously, and some of the people from adjoining cottages had gathered in the house.

He could not, however, find anyone who knew of any child in the district answering to his description. In fact, there was no one who even remotely resembled the little director on the road during the night.

Then, an old woman spoke up. "She did have a son, but that was many years ago. He was a wild bit of a laddie and would be a mature man now . . . but he ran away and joined the army.

He didn't keep up with her . . . and he got killed in the war".

The following occurrence happened, however, not in a country cottage, but in a stately mansion, seat of a powerful and prosperous landed family, who were also Roman Catholic, and it was ultimately possible to identify the spectre concerned.

The library of this particular house was reputed to be haunted, and finally the owner of the house, on the advice of a friend, decided to do something about it and approached a certain priest, who agreed to spend a night in the place.

The room concerned was large and heavily furnished, with its shelves well stocked, and an expensive selection of gilt-framed pictures around the walls, while its French windows looked over a rolling expanse of carefully tended lawns and herbaceous borders, peppered by the mighty oaks, chestnuts and sycamore trees.

The clerical watcher was shown there and left with ample sustenance in the way of food and he settled himself into a comfortably cushioned chair in front of a blazing fire.

Gradually, the lights in the various parts of the house began to be extinguished, and he sat there for some time, reading. Ultimately, he turned to the thermos pot of coffee and to the selection of sandwiches and cake, following which he said his night prayers before stirring up the fire and returning to his book.

Slowly, the flames of the fire began to die back and he put on more coal before settling down into the large armchair, as he thought, for the night.

Sleep, however, eluded him and before long he felt the temperature of the room begin to fall, and he drew his cape tightly around him, but, nevertheless, the atmospheric chill steadily developed into what felt almost like an antarctic night.

Then he noticed the pallid, expressionless face of a figure standing in one of the library alcoves.

The troubled ghost selects a particular book

Apart from the bitter cold, the one reading lamp that he left on seemed to have dimmed in brilliance, but he was still able to distinguish that the figure, now looking so directly at him, was that of a clergyman.

The occupant of the armchair plucked up all his courage, although the phantom appeared perfectly benign, and composing himself before rising to his feet, he addressed it in the name of the Most High and Eternal Trinity and bade him say what it was that disturbed him and why he was seen repeatedly in this place.

The ghost did not reply, but glided across the floor towards some bookshelves and pointed to a certain volume, before turning the gaunt, white face, almost pathetically, towards his interrogator, as if to make sure that he was paying attention.

Then he seemed to tap the book several times with his long, bony finger, making no doubt of the emphasis that he was placing on that particular tome. Finally, he bowed slightly, as if in deference, and disappeared.

Going over to those bookshelves, the observer immediately removed the volume that had been indicated and, from the title printed on the cover, recognised that he was familiar with it and knew it to be a most innocuous publication.

Opening it, he noticed that the pages contained a thin sheet of notepaper which had some writing on it, and which appeared to have been used as a bookmark.

Glancing over the writing, however, he was astounded to find that the words constituted what was obviously someone's confession. He could not understand it, so he deliberately crumpled up the paper and threw it into the depths of the dying fire, standing back to watch the flames rise around it and quickly consume it.

Then, resuming his seat in the armchair, he endeavoured to settle down for the rest of the night, and although he did not manage to actually sleep, at least there was no further intrusion.

In the morning he told exactly what had happened to the master of the house, who heard him in amazement.

He in turn, then added that the household used to have their own chaplain, and at that time, for some reason or other, the confessions were usually heard in the library.

"I can understand that," commented the priest, "but I still can't fathom why there should be a written confession and why it should be in that particular book".

"I can", the master added quietly, "my uncle was a deaf mute. He always wrote his down".

"And do you think that the chaplain may not have destroyed it?"

"Yes, that seems possible. He possibly put it in the book he was reading, meaning to destroy it later . . . and forgot all about it. Perhaps it was summer and the fire wasn't on, or maybe he was disturbed and called out suddenly. Oh, I can think of many reasons".

"Possibly so. In any case we'll know if we're right".

They were, because to my knowledge, the ghost of the library was never seen again.

Glaistigs, urisks, trows and merfolk

The majority of reports concerning the existence or behaviour of the Glaistig seem to stem mainly from the near off-shore islands, such as Mull, Arran and Skye, or from the part of the mainland that is directly opposite to them.

This creature is said to have once been mortal, but since then has become, either completely, or partly esconced with the nature of the fairy, although maintaining many of the human characteristics, especially those concerning dwelling habits and a fondness for certain inhabited places.

There does not appear to be any malice with the Glaistig, who, like the Banshee, is nearly always referred to in the feminine, perhaps because it is known to have a liking, and a talent, for carrying out routine domestic chores, but it is also known to keep a watch over cattle in the fields or over sheep on the hills, while in the main, its visitations seem to be mainly nocturnal.

One account that I have been given, comes from an area not far from Oban, and depicts this entity as a rather warm, sentimental creature with a strong attachment to a certain house.

In this particular case, it was generally believed that she was once mistress of this handsome residence and that for several generations she had adopted a sort of watching brief over its inhabitants.

On several occasions the family distinctly heard the loud wailing, very similar again, to the Banshee in Ireland, whenever misfortune was about to befall them, but there were also many instances of it assisting them when trouble threatened and protecting them from danger.

In addition to this, she had often actually been seen sitting at a certain place and watching over the cattle grazing in the surrounding fields, just like some benevolent mistress of the estate.

At one time, the family decided, to more or less demolish the old house and replace it with a new, modern edifice, but this intention seemed to greatly disturb the mystic resident.

During the night, for many months, there was the sound of footsteps on the stairs and the scraping of furniture being moved around, in fact, all the noises of a traditional haunting.

The whole exposition seemed to worsen as the time of the demolition approached, ultimately culminating in a loud, persistent and plaintive wailing as the new building began to take shape, but when it actually became ready for complete occupation, the noises stopped, never to be heard again, nor was there any other record of her being seen anywhere on the estate.

The long sessions of watching over cattle form the basis of several tales about the Glaistig, when it has been known to take the shape of several other animals, but most often a fierce dog, in order to protect its charges from marauders. In general, it is not a very well known entity, but it is mainly benign, with some sort of sensitive affection towards a family or premises, while there are few, if any, reports of it being in any way spiteful, malicious, or in any way harmful.

★　　★　　★　　★　　★

Another of the lesser known mystical inhabitants of the Highlands is the Urisk, who differs in almost every characteristic from the Glaistig. This creature is rarely seen, as its normal habitats are solitary, remote and lonely places, but eye witness reports tell us that it is large in stature, greyish in colour, stolid and rather stupid in disposition, but of a mulish, harmless nature, who makes little secret of the fact that he doesn't seek company.

It is generally in the evening when this entity is seen, and usually at a fair distance from where it will sit well back on a rock or hillock and view the passer-by from afar.

Again, there are very few accounts describing any form of communication with human beings, who have had the unusual experience of coming up close to one, but there have been some and there have even been one or two where they have encountered some hostility from the creature.

This, however, seems to be completely out of character, and the general pattern is mainly one of complete avoidance, and watching any intruder from a very safe distance.

Most of the tales describing the Urisk come from the southern part of the Highlands, namely from around Perthshire or Argyllshire, although there are some from Lochaber.

One account, that I have received, comes from the vicinity of Tyndrum, a village on the Road to the Isles, and just south of Rannoch Moor, where a Urisk was observed to follow the same pattern as the deer, as it would be seen on the high mountain slopes during the summer and down in the lower pastures during the severe weather of a winter. .

A favourite place for it to be seen was sitting on a rock beside a waterfall and this is now known in the Gaelic, as 'The Urisk's Cascade'.

Again, at Glen Mallie in Lochaber, there is a ravine that has long had the reputation of being haunted by a Urisk, and is so named in the Gaelic, whereas the Urisk of Ben Loy, near the border of Perthshire, was also frequently seen sitting on a stone beside a waterfall and this rock is also known to this day as 'The Urisk's Stone'.

There is a traditional tale of several Urisks being around the southern shore of the Lake of Menteith, near Aberfoyle, and it is said that they were, on one occasion, employed as labourers by a former Earl.

Their task was to fashion the small peninsula, known as Arnmauk, which protrudes from the southern shore of the Lake towards the Island of Inchmahome.

Whether he was very pleased with the job they did, or perhaps he wanted to keep on friendly terms with them, but he rewarded them by presenting them with a hollow well, up on the north side of Ben Venue.

It is not known whether this was a place of their choice, but it certainly seems to possess some advantages for a forum of assembly, as it is surrounded by many large boulders and overhung with trees, so to this day it is known as The Corrie of the Urisks.

The mermaid drags him into the deep waters

At this spot it was commonly believed that the solemn meeting of all the Urisks in Scotland used to be held, but with the creeping advance of habitation, and the increase in tourism with the popularity of hill walking, they have now moved off to some other suitable location in an even more isolated place.

★   ★   ★   ★   ★

In the folklore of the Orkney and Shetland Islands, a creature which is the subject of a number of tales, is called a Trow. In many aspects its behaviour is similar to that of the Wee Folk on the mainland. They are reputed to have an ardent love and talent for music and also to possess the skill and agility for excellent dancing, while the main difference seems to be in stature. Several accounts describe them as being quite violent.

Towards the centre of the Island of Papa Stour, Shetland, there are several mounds which are regarded by the locals as being ancient settlements of the Trows, and many of the older people tend to avoid them, especially after dark.

In his book, 'Folk-tales and Legends of Shetland', John Nicolson tells of a woman, who, on a night near Christmas time, when there was much moonlight, would stand on the brig-stanes at the front of her house and watch the Trows as they danced on the green sward near to the shore.

On several occasions, she invited her husband to join her and observe the performance, but he invariably could not see anything unless he held his wife's hand, or placed his foot on top of hers.

Tradition also has it, that the Trows at Birrafirth built their 'brocht' or castle with stones that were taken from Papa Stour, transporting them over the Sound by raft, and this belief arises from the fact that one of the rafts, loaded with large stones, is seen at low tide, where it was reputed to have run aground during the operation.

One saying that is quite common amongst the older people on the Orkney Islands when they are sending a child out for a message after dark, is "Don't be afraid! All the Trows are drowned now".

This saying comes from a legend, whereby the Trows were said to be flitting from the Black Craig of Stromness to take up residence amongst the Hills of Hoy, and the time of the removal was around midnight, on a night when there was a full moon.

To negotiate the Sound they used a long rope of plaited straw which parted when they were around midstream, and they were cast into the surging water.

★   ★   ★   ★   ★

In the North Western coastal districts of Scotland, particularly around the County of Sutherland and also in some of the Hebridean Islands, a belief in the Merfolk, who are considered to be the traditional inhabitants of the sea, still exists amongst some of the people.

Most of the accounts from the annals of folklore concern mermaids, who are reputed to come up occasionally from their underwater sea caves and either recline on the shore, or strike a pose on a partly submerged rock, while combing their beautifully long hair, and often singing in resonance with the low moaning of the sea wind.

The common superstition is that if ever one was taken unawares and caught by a mortal, the mermaid had the power to grant three wishes, provided that she was released and allowed to return to the ocean's depths, but generally there is a fear and a dread of even seeing one of them.

★　　　★　　　★　　　★　　　★

From the Island of Benbecula comes the story of a little sea maiden who was seen happily frolicking in the rough water that almost continually laps noisily on the rock-spurred shore, and she was observed for some time by a group of people, before suddenly being struck by a stone that was thrown by a local youth.

Some days later it is said that her body was washed up onto the strand and it was decreed by one of the local officials that she be buried in a coffin, after being dressed in the customary burial clothes, and all this was carried out with every dignity.

A grave in the cemetery at Nunton, not so far from where the waters of the Atlantic break on the shore, is reputed to be the last resting place of the little sea maiden.

★　　　★　　　★　　　★　　　★

In Loch Torridon there is a small island on which very few people have landed over the years, and it is commonly called 'Eilean-nan-Sithean', or the 'Fairy Isle'.

The inhabitants of the nearby hamlet do not make use of its rich pasture and the local belief is that it is an undesirable place, being haunted by the spirit of evil, while on many an evening the wind has a peculiar eerie wail as it sweeps across the water and around the contours of the deserted isle.

The story is that there once was a fisherman who came on a mermaid in these waters, fell in love with her and went off with her for a time, but he ultimately tired of her way of life and left her.

She was deeply hurt and the only feeling now with her was one of vengeance towards him.

Now, one of the most common ruses of the merfolk towards human beings is to lure them towards danger and it was some time before an opportunity presented itself to this mermaid.

She arranged some false diversion that set him off his correct course and onto the rocks so that his boat was wrecked and he was not long struggling in the water before she dragged him down into its depths.

Nowadays, the strangest thing about this deserted and silent place is that its very atmosphere has a heavy sense of eeriness, while its terrain is completely devoid of bird or animal life.

SCOTTISH SHIPWRECK

AND

DISASTER STORIES

Victims of the black storm

By J.M. RUSSELL

The voice from the tape recorder made compulsive listening as it recalled vividly Eyemouth's Disaster Day in 1881. Mrs Jane Swanston made the tape in 1970 at the age of 96 at a family party with the recorder placed on the floor beside her.

Now we were sitting around the same chair with two members of the family listening to the recording.

She told how on the forenoon of Friday, October 14, 1881, the bright sunny schoolrooms were suddenly cast in heavy gloom and a raging wind struck terror into the panicking children. Seven-year-old Jane, in common with all the pupils, was sent home.

Her voice trembled, as she related: "It was terrible. I saw twae boats smashed on the rocks." Then came a reference to the "Forward" being driven all the way to Norway, and "My ain faither was washed ashore at Marshall Meadows." (Near Berwick-on-Tweed).

Jane's father was William Scott on the "Forget-Me-Not" which went down with all her crew.

"It was an awful day, 129 men lost. Ma faither's uncle George Scott and his three sons John, George and William all lost in the sea wi' the 'Beautiful Star'."

The voice on the tape continued telling of the grief of weeping men and women as they searched the rocks and sought news of their families. Then came these poignant sentences: "Euphie Scott was asking, 'Is George no comin' back?' She broke her heart and never came over the bed again."

Thus went on the recollections of the old lady who died in 1974 in her 100th year. Moving as they were, her words could not describe all of the heartbreak, heroism and sheer terror of a disaster which widowed 73 women and left 262 children fatherless. Of the 45 fishing boats that sailed out of Eyemouth, only 26 returned.

On that morning more than a century ago the fishermen of Eyemouth were in a quandry. The early morning sunshine was brilliant, the sky cloudless and the sea calm — but the glass was falling! To sail or not to sail? The Eyemouth fishermen decided to go. Along the coast, the Berwick-upon-Tweed men stayed in their harbour.

Only nine miles out, the haddock lines were busy when, not long before midday, a strange stillness fell over the area. From bright sunshine the day turned black as night. Within minutes, a howling hurricane shrieked and tore into the boats. The sea became a cauldron of turbulent, snarling water with waves, seemingly mountain high, crashing down up on the boats. Sails were shredded like paper, masts smashed or torn from the deck, ropes and rigging swept away. Some boats, with their ballasts shifting, capsized almost immediately, others were simply smashed to pieces under the weight of the raging seas. Boats were blown right out of the water, while others turned turtle. The awesome ferocity of the storm was to continue unabated for 25 hours.

By noon, all the folk of Eyemouth, in a panic of fear at the howling inferno which enveloped them, were lining the shore, rocks and cliff-tops searching for the fleet. Blinded by flying spray and in the terrible black mirk, the watchers could see nothing.

At last the first Fifie to reach the River Eye, the "Onward", arrived in spectacular fashion. Unable to see because of the "smoke" or blinding spray, Skipper Andrew Dougal was clinging desperately to the helm as the boat flew before the wind straight towards the rocks. When the crash came, however, the "Onward" found herself on the top of the harbour-bank!

Alas, the skipper had to report the loss of his own son Alex, washed overboard two miles from home.

Anxious eyes now saw the "Britannia" and the "Alabama" clear the Hurcars, the natural rock breakwater which normally protects Eyemouth, but which presented a fearsome trap in those seas. Somehow they made harbour. Then followed the tragic drama of the "Harmony" which was driven on to the rocks behind the breakwater at the mouth of the harbour and smashed to smithereens. Similarly the "Radient" was crushed under a weight of water and sank within yards of the shore.

Both crews were lost, the death cries of the fishermen mingling with the shrieks of helpless wives and mothers watching from the shore. Efforts at life-saving were futile, rockets and weighted-ropes being thrown back like matches in the face of the gale. On land, no one could stand upright. Men and women clawed their way among rocks on their hands and knees.

Later came one of the most remarkable escapes of Disaster Day. The "Pilgrim" was caught by a gigantic wave which threw her on the rocks at Fort Point. A second huge following wave lifted her off the rocks and over the Black Carr to land safely on shore.

The only white-sailed ship to sail, the "Press Home", on her maiden voyage, fought her way desperately through the turmoil of seas and seemed to have battled to safety when, her ballast shifting, she shot upwards out of the water by the bow. She helled over and all her crew were thrown into the sea. The three brothers Stott were among them. One had just been married the previous week and his bride witnessed the tragedy.

All day long news of Eyemouth boats lost or miraculously saved, came from adjoining Burnmouth, from Berwick and the beach of Spittal. "The Blossom", grounded at Goswick in a terrible condition, was finally reached by coastguards and local fishermen after fighting the elements for hours. Only two men were still aboard. Daniel Stevenson lived but John Burgon did not survive.

262 orphans of black storm.

Came Friday night and Eyemouth was a town in the depth of despair with all hope fast disappearing for those still at sea.

Saturday brought better news and renewed hope that "Enterprise", "Success", "White Star" and "Economy" had struggled into South Shields.

On Sunday morning at 4 a.m. Robert Young, himself saved on the Friday when the "James and Robert" was thrown up on the rocks to the south of Burnmouth harbour, was on look-out at the Fort on the promontory to the north of Eyemouth. Suddenly he saw a boat bearing down on the town. Running through the streets he shouted the good news. Within minutes the shore and quay were lined with folk, most of them in their nightwear. For some it was to mean heartfelt relief, for others deepening hopelessness. The "Ariel Gazelle" limped into the harbour, battered and broken, under makeshift sails which had been torn to ribbons. She had been 45 hours at sea.

Having come through the ordeal of Disaster Day, the "Ariel Gazelle" crew stuck together and were photographed in 1920, almost 40 years later. During the day, men who had come from South Shields by train brought further news of tragedies at sea. George "Little Dod" Collins, skipper of the "White Star", was interviewed on his arrival home. He told of the first signs of the coming storm.

"There was great smoke (blinding spray) and near darkness."

He told how the "Myrtle" was seen to be struck by heavy seas and turn turtle and again how they had passed another boat bottom-up. Finding it impossible to make for port, they shifted the ballast to the front to the boat, the better to meet the waves and "to have the sea for our friend for the night." After 44 hours at sea, 25 of them in this ghastly gale, the "White Star" reached Shields and safety. "Little Dod" was habourmaster for 10 years following his retiral from the sea.

Came the sabbath and the churches had congregations in dire distress and grief even among those who were able to give prayers of thankfulness for the safe return of their own folk. Empty seats carried their eloquent message of death. Just as this sad day was about to end, at midnight came the heavy rumble of hurrying feet on the cobbled streets. Once more joy came to lessen the tragedy — for some, at least. The crew of the "Fisher Lassies" were home all except one, William Young, swept overboard on the Friday. They had reached Shields on the Sunday night, too late to wire the news to Eyemouth, but in time to catch the train to Burnmouth and finish the journey on foot. Imagine the shock and heartbreak for the wife of William Young!

On the fourth day, Monday, a telegram arrived telling of the safe arrival at North Shields of the "Welcome Home", skippered by one of Eyemouth's best-known fishermen William "Tarry" Maltman.

Tuesday and Wednesday brought no further survivors and Eyemouth finally accepted the sorrowful fact that those still missing would not return.

A total of 189 fishermen from the East Coast were lost that terrible day and 129 of them were from Eyemouth.

I have been retold many stories by older descendants of Disaster Day families.

Mrs Teenie Dougal (Maltman) said: "My father, Thomas Maltman, was 11 on Disaster Day. His father, my grandfather, was 'Tarry' Maltman of the "Welcome Home". He was saved, but he lost his son, George. Like all the other children, my father was sent home when the storm started. Houses were empty and no food made that day, with all the mothers out searching for news of their men. With grief everywhere around them, some of the boys escaped it and the gale by huddling together in the hold of a boat laid up just beyond the wooden bridge that spanned the River Eye at the time.

A horse-drawn baker's cart came abreast the boat, the wind caught the horse and it fell, the cart tilted and the boys were showered with scones and cookies. 'Eat them up boys, I can't sell them now!' said the driver. The story was often told to us at the fireside when we were children and my father used to say it was like a miracle the way they were all fed."

Another relative told how Eyemouth was at the peak of its success at the time of the disaster with a population of 2,935, of which 1,000 were employed in some form of fishing industry. Three hundred of them were fishermen.

The disaster cut the fleet almost in half. After five months searching, only 30 bodies were recovered.

Blunders as 227 die
in worst rail disaster

By EDWIN S. TOWILL

It all happened a long time ago, when the old man who is writing this was a little boy of six and when things were much simpler, with no atom bombs or astronauts. The boy wakened earlier than usual that morning and looked out on Scotland Road, the historic Great North Road which, within the next twenty-five years would become one of the busiest and most dangerous highways in England. In the year 1915, however, traffic was so light, even on this main road, cattle and geese might be driven down the hill from the suburb of Stanwix and over the bridge into the city of Carlisle to market without undue danger.

On that morning of May 22, 1915, the Great War was still in its first year and for so many people life was going on normally except for the absence of so many young men who had joined up in Kitchener's Army. A little after seven o' clock when the boy looked out of his window he sensed that something unusual and not within the normal experience of small boys was taking place. The street was much busier than usual. At first there were just a few cars all (after the fashion of that day) open tourers. Then came more and more until they were a great stream, all heading north, out of the town toward the Border at Gretna just five miles away. They were being driven very fast and making a great deal of noise for in place of the slow, deep-throated bulb horn, then usual, the drivers had evidently been supplied with police whistles which were being sounded continuously to clear a path.

For a while the boy watched the cars until he sensed that every available vehicle in the town was taking part; then gradually the cars grew less until in half an hour hardly a car was to be seen. Sleep overcame curiosity and the boy got back into bed, but before long the noise on the road began again — with one difference — this time the cars were all heading south into the city, and in each car, sitting or lying beside the driver was huddled a lifeless figure, not dressed in ordinary clothes, but either in a torn and stained kharki tunic, or simply covered by torn sheets soaked in blood.

Before the last cars passed and the road became quiet again, the boy had watched over three hundred dead and wounded, casualties from the most tragic of all British rail accidents which had taken place early that morning just a few miles from his house over the Scottish Border. At the time, and for some years afterwards, the child was spared the gruesome details of what had happened. Only much later, when he grew up and went for a time to work in the port of Leith was he able to piece together the full picture, for the special troop train in which the majority of the dead and injured had been travelling was the third of four trains conveying the Seventh Royal Scots to Liverpool for embarkation to France.

Some rail accidents have been caused by defects or failure in the signalling system, others by excessive speed or poor permanent way, still others by an error of judgement or momentary lapse by driver, signalman or one of the station staff.

The causes of this disaster, however, were far more complicated and much less excusable than any one of these. The failure of two signalmen to obey working regulations and carry out their elementary duties was followed by a whole series of mistakes which culminated in their forgetting that the local passenger train from Carlisle had been left standing outside their signal box at Quintinshill, just north of the Scottish Border, while under clear signals, a heavy "troop special" of 21 vehicles was bearing down upon it at full speed from the north and on the adjacent "Down" track from the south the night express from Euston, of 15 heavy corridor and sleeping cars had been signalled and was almost due to pass.

The position was that at that moment express trains from north and south were approaching Quintinshill and would pass each other at high speed — a fact of railway working which happened many times each day and to which no one gave a second thought. The one fact which was different on that morning was that the signalman responsible, James

227 die in worst rail disaster.

Tinsley, seemed to have completely forgotten that he already had the local train from Carlisle standing on the "up" track; the very line over which the troop special was signalled to travel.

There was still one faint chance that a disaster might be avoided. If the crew of the troop train were keeping a sharp lookout they might see the local in time to apply their brakes and perhaps stop in time; unfortunately, however, a long train of empty coal wagons waiting on the loop of the relief line completely obscured the view and they saw no reason why they should apply the brakes.

The first horrific impact was when the Caledonian 4-4-0 loco No. 121 struck the stationary No. 907 head on. The 907 was a big "Cardean" class engine which was only on the little train that day being "run-in" after an overhaul. The fact that the standing train had its brakes full on greatly increased the damage and the four vehicles were impelled to set off on their own down the line with two of the passengers dead through the shock of the collision. The coaches of the troop train telescoped until the train was only about half its original length. Soldiers who had survived staggered out onto the track thinking to reach safety but quite unaware that at that moment the London express had passed Gretna and was upon them.

In a moment we shall return to the scene of the smash and examine its causes but meantime we shall return to the little boy whose memories we have been recording. Some years later when he was grown up he chanced to go north to work for a time in Leith where he found that memories of the Gretna Disaster were still very vivid in many homes — Leith folk considered the Seventh Royal Scots as their own regiment. Faded pictures of sons, husbands and lovers stood on the mantlepieces of the small tenement homes and in nearby Rosebank Cemetery the memorial to those killed in the disaster was still fresh and new looking.

Soldiers who survived that day must be all dead now but in the intervening years the boy at the window — grown to manhood as little boys do — met and became friends with some of those who had survived. The headmaster of an Edinburgh school, whom he got to know well, never seemed to enjoy normal good health and always walked with a decided limp. One day he revealed almost casually in conversation that it was the result of the smash, but he didn't grumble for of all those in his compartment only he had been left alive. Another survivor, when his family left the district, presented me with a gruesome relic — an officer's bayonet still bright and shining in its scabbard and apparently perfect until looked at sideways, when one could see how the steel had been bent to the shape of its wearer's leg and hip. After the initial impact the young officer had been flung onto the ballast as the whole carriage above him became splintered wood and metal. Then as he lay unable to move there came a grinding of brakes and showers of white hot ashes and sparks rose in the air above him as the loco and front coach ploughed over the tops of the wrecked cars of the troop train and what little was left of the "local". He was fortunate in having been flung down to comparative safety away from the still moving wheels. Some 500 others on the three trains had not been so lucky for the final total, which was never more than a careful estimate, gave 227 killed and an even greater number injured.

We have reserved till the end any explanation of how this greatest of all rail disasters happened on a line as well protected by safety devices as any in the country. Punctually at 6.10 that morning Carlisle Citadel Station signalled away the local which was to precede the express which was running some 30 minutes late. The earlier down express had got away before the "Local" and would be well into Dumfriesshire. The local was sent off but would be shunted somewhere down the line to let the express past. This was standard practice and had been done several times before when an express was running late. Quintinshill was a suitable place to do this as it possessed "relief" or "passing loops" beside both "up" and "down" running lines. Here slower trains might wait to allow expresses to overtake.

Unfortunately, owing to the volume of war traffic both loops were that morning occupied with waiting freight trains and so the signalman decided to shunt the local to the main "up", where it would not block the down express. It would, of course, then be directly in the path of the troop train from the north. But after the express was safely out of the way he would move it back to its proper line and allow the special through. In case, by some mischance a signalman might forget that he had a vehicle standing in such a position on the wrong line a special regulation, known to all signalmen, laid down that a set of large rubber collars should be taken from the drawer and hung on the signal levers. It would be extremely difficult to ignore these and almost impossible to pull the signals to clear. If the signalman had obeyed this rule the troop train would have been brought to a stop and there would have been no accident. The man concerned that morning, James Tinsley, who seemed to be paying little attention to what was going on on the lines outside his box had already broken one rule. The time laid down to take over from his night shift mate, Meakin, was 5 a.m. but the two men had a private and unauthorised agreement that the day man could get a lift along on the "local" and the changeover would be made when the train arrived about 6.30. There was no intrinsic danger in such private arrangements but they were frowned on by the higher officials and they evidently did lead to loose working for on the morning concerned Tinsley was not alone in the box as he should have been; Meakin was there reading the morning's war news, and some of the other railmen were going in and out.

Tinsley apparently quite forgot about the local standing where he could have looked down at it, right outside his box. When asked by Kirkpatrick, the next box northwards, if he would accept the troop train he immediately did so and pulled off all signals to give it a clear passage, and a moment later when the bell from Gretna called he accepted the express from the south. For it, of course, the down line was still clear, but before it reached the fatal spot the troop and the local train had collided and a mass of debris, including a loco tender lay blocking the route of the express. At the last moment Tinsley realised his error and set the signals back at danger, but it was much too late.

For what could only be considered culpable carelessness he was given a term of imprisonment where he was joined by Meakin who had to share at least part of the blame. For some time local papers were full of suggestions from laymen with many wild or impractical ideas as to how the Caledonian Company should run its trains.

And the little boy who as an elderly man has given his memories in this article never passed the Quintinshill loops without lowering the carriage window a little and removing his cap. Recently this has become more difficult; the signal cabin is now away and the loops are, I believe, removed. Soon it will be difficult to locate the place. It will be gone, like the bad dream that it was.

The Giant Cholera

By JOHN R. SMITH

St. Michael's Churchyard in Dumfries must be one of the most visited graveyards in Scotland. Most admirers of Robert Burns waste no time in making their way to the white Mausoleum which displays itself in sharp contrast to the greyness of the memorials to the less famous. Some, though, turn aside from the common path to sense something of the atmosphere which a town churchyard must convey — the history of the people captured in stone. One or two of the more adventurous may come across a long, green plot, surrounded by a fence, and with a single stone in explanation. They will be surprised to read that this is the last resting place of most of the 420 inhabitants of the town who died in the autumn of 1832. How did such a disaster occur?

The early days of September 1832 held little enough excitement for the burghers of Dumfries. Life was steady — as was appropriate for a quiet, country town. People from the surrounding farms and villages came and went, bringing their produce for sale and buying the luxuries which the town had to offer. Market day brought a temporary bustle in the middle of the week. The arrival of the mail coaches occasioned an interest in the doings of fashionable society or of the London politicians, but apart from providing topics for eager discussion in the ale-houses and the drawing-rooms, events outside their own little world seemed to have little noticeable effect on the townspeople.

Still, there was one potentially dramatic event scheduled for that month — an event which overshadowed even the unpredictable thundery weather, and the serious accident to the Portpatrick mail on the second Thursday of the month. For on the Friday — the 14th — the people of the town were to be treated to a rare and wonderful spectacle. Mr. Green, the "celebrated aeronaut," was to make an ascent in his balloon from the yard of the King's Arms.

It was expected that such an unusual and exciting display would attract a large crowd, and so it did. The streets surrounding the yard of the inn were thronged with folk in high holiday mood. Those who were deprived of a good view headed for nearby hills. Space at the top windows of buildings was at a premium. Many families had flocked in from the countryside to see this event which would defy nature.

Mr. Green duly ascended and descended. The crowd marvelled, and went home. Among the curious was one Mary Paterson, a middle-aged, respectable shopkeeper from English Street. She watched with just as much excitement as the rest, although she did feel very tired since she had just finished a large washing before coming to view the spectacle. When she got home she felt much worse, and took to her bed. Perhaps, her neighbours thought, it was the result of becoming too excited, and then catching a chill in the open air after the hot work of the weekly wash. But her suffering grew worse, causing great anxiety among the inhabitants of the poor lodging-house of the area. So great a crowd formed that a town's officer had to be called to restore order at the Paterson house. A few hours later she was dead. The doctors who attended her were in no doubt as to what was the cause of this sudden demise. Cholera had come to Dumfries.

For months now the name of this disease had been on everyone's lips. Almost a year before that fateful day in Dumfries the first British case of cholera had appeared in Sunderland, having slowly spread from Asia through the normal channels of travel and commerce. Like most other towns, Dumfries had cause to fear for its safety. The combination of crowded housing, undernourishment and poor drainage and scavenging provided a natural breeding ground for disease. Worse still, almost all the water used for drinking and domestic purposes was carried by four old men in barrels from the River Nith, and was sold round the doors at five canfuls for a penny. The nature of this water is described by a Dumfries writer to lived through the epidemic:

"The river, when swelled by heavy rains, which was often the case, became thick with mud, and it was constantly exposed to a more noxious pollution, caused by the refuse poured into it from the town.

"The quality of the water did not improve by being borne about in barrels of suspicious aspect, and, indeed, the liquid drawn from them during the summer acquired a taste-me-not repulsiveness by the presence of innumerable little objects, pleasant to none save an enthusiast in entomology."

Ofcourse, little could be done about that overnight, but a Board of Health was formed which immediately organised soup kitchens for the poor in an attempt to help them resist infection. Old tenements and closes were scrubbed out with hot lime. The folk of Dumfries may have been reassured by all this, but the Medical Faculty was more realistic. Through the Board of Health the surgeons began to arrange a store of spirits and laudanum. Canvas beds for removing patients to hospital were prepared.

Another victim is carried away for burial.

Every edition of the local paper seemed to carry fresh news of the spread of "the Giant Cholera." Columns were devoted to dreadful stories of cases and incidents in England, and then in Stirling, Kilmarnock, Haddington and Musselburgh. There were reports of guards being posted on the roads into Edinburgh, and of children left orphaned and homeless. The people of Dumfries must have been confused by the many pieces of advice with which they were bombarded for the sake of their health. "Keep your feet dry and warm — wear a belt of good warm flannel round your bowels . . . have the mind firmly resolved and courageous," advised one columnist.

Typically, great emphasis was placed on the need for abstemious living. Almost every cholera report carried the news of fresh victims who had "got themselves brutally intoxicated" or who were "broken down by long, continued and ruinous excesses."

On September 18 the *Dumfries Courier* was still carrying reports of the disease in Glasgow and Edinburgh, but there was no mention of the death of Mary Paterson. However, when a week had passed and the newspaper was again published there was no further question of attempting to hide the truth. The town was firmly in the grip of the "pestilence."

The normally unruffled Doonhammers were first of all incredulous and then panicky. The very name of the disease carried overtones of the unknown and the fearful. The Dumfries Infirmary, which had done so much to preserve life in the fever epidemics earlier in the century, flatly refused to accept cholera cases, and an inadequate hospital was set up in a granary in English Street. As the days passed and the number of cases increased, individuals began to hide symptoms in order to avoid being removed to the cholera hospital, and the *Dumfries Courier* waded in on the side of public spirit and decency.

Wild rumours spread. Had the town been infected because Mary Paterson had accepted a gift of second-hand clothes from a cholera victim in London? (The clothing had, in fact, come from an entirely disease-free locality.) The hardest-hit part of the town was the squalid area of closely-housed vennels and narrow stairs bounded by English Street and Shakespeare Street, but it wasn't long before the fashionable mansions of Buccleuch Street were just as aware of the presence of the disease. Dr. McCracken, who, just a few days previously had been advertising his medicinal wares for the cure of "inward wasting, lowness of spirits and sexual debility," went the way of so many of his patients.

With every succeeding day, the toll worsened. September 26 — nine new cases, five deaths; on the 28th — sixty-eight new cases and nineteen deaths. Then — incredibly in a population of only ten thousand — on October 2, there were fifty-five new cases and forty-four deaths.

It's not hard to imagine the scenes in the town. One reads of events in contemporary accounts. Fear had emptied the streets, the only regular travellers being the doctors — and they were so weary that they had to ride the few yards journey from house to house. Funerals were hastily assembled and were largely shunned by mourners because of the fear of infection. As soon as the last breath left a body, the corpse was placed in a ready-made coffin. With only the hospital-bearers in attendance, and with the relatives following at a safe distance, the remains were taken up to St. Michael's to be added to the fast growing pile in the communal grave.

The grave-diggers worked constantly, extending the trench, and sprinkling quicklime on each fresh tier. Sunday worship no longer took place in the church. The worshippers had been driven away by their fear of the cholera grave.

Dumfries had become a place to be avoided. The country people no longer came to market, and the annual Rood Fair was cancelled. Any individuals who fled the town for safety were greeted coolly — if at all. A letter sent by a man in Dumfries to a friend in Galloway was put in an outhouse for three days before anyone would approach it. In Lockerbie a passing vagrant died. They had to pay men twelve shillings (60 pence) each to bury the body.

The death toll continued to mount. Thomas Thorburn, tanner; Margaret Lawson, dressmaker; George Thomson, tailor; John McGhie, doctor. He would tell that tale no more of how his grandfather single-handedly drove the Young Pretender and his followers from Dumfries, by unwittingly bringing a false report of the advance of the English army.

All the elements of tragedy were present. Many families were left without father or mother, including the ten children of Alex. McLure, stockingmaker. Within the space of a few hours, three brothers found themselves widowed. The head jailer, wine merchant, even the sexton who dug the graves, all had their names added to the sad list. Every possible remedy was tried, including the burning of tar barrels in the streets in an attempt to disinfect the atmosphere.

The religious possibilities in the delivery of such an "awful warning" were not to be overlooked either. Tracts were published to outline the error of their ways to sinners and to the unconverted, and a day of fast and humiliation was held in every church in the burgh. This spiritual interpretation of events seemed to be aided by a peculiar atmospheric phenomenon which had occurred during the first ten days of the epidemic. The adjoining burghs of Dumfries and Maxwelltown were overlaid by a thick cloud that gave the appearance from the surrounding hills of a funeral pall, and successfully kept the light of the sun from the death-filled streets below. It produced such a feeling of gloom and despondency, the widespread opinion that Dumfries was being visited by an avenging angel seemed quite justified.

At last, when things could get no worse, they began to improve. Slowly at first, and then with increasing certainty, the daily reports grew better, until there were only one or two deaths each day—and then finally none. The epidemic had lasted for two months and had ravaged a town which had felt secure in its peace and prosperity. The cholera hospital was closed, as was the House of Refuge which had sheltered the families of the victims. The cholera pit in St Michael's Churchyard was finally filled in, covering at least 350 bodies. Fotry years later William

McDowall, historian of Dumfries, was to report that the turf on that sad place was "kept green even in winter by the rich soil below."

With similar morbid interest, the survivors of the epidemic read the autopsy reports in the local newspaper, and the arguments of the Medical Faculty as to the nature of this disease which had attacked them. They understood little beyond the fact that well over a thousand of the inhabitants of the burghs of Dumfries and Maxwelltown had fallen ill, and that official figures said that 548 had died, although the true figure was probably much higher.

It took another attack of cholera sixteen years later to force the council to take action against the real culprit—the water supply. During the second epidemic 431 died. It was then decided to pipe in water from Lochrutton Loch—news which was greeted by the ringing of bells, the burning of bonfires and general acclamation. The cry of the ancient "burndrawers"—the men who brought the water from the River Nith— was at last silenced. As far as the townspeople of Dumfries were concerned, the threat from the "Giant Cholera" was at an end.

Cinema deaths should never have happened

By IAN ANSDELL

In the years between the wars there was no bigger treat for a youngster than a visit to the movies. The flickering screen revealed a thrilling world where wild west lawmen beat the baddies, clean-cut heroes foiled fiendish villains, and spacemen battled with strange monsters on the threshold of the galaxy.

The children who thronged into the Glen Cinema in Paisley for a matinee performance on the last Tuesday afternoon of 1929 had even more than that to be excited about.

Being Hogmanay, the memory of Christmas was fresh in their minds and the prospect of returning to school still deliciously distant.

By the time the lights dimmed and the first reel of a cowboy film, 'Desperado Dude', began to cast its spell, the Glen was packed.

Originally a meeting place for the Independent Order of Good Templars, the building had been licensed as a cinema in 1910. Its ground floor hall, measuring some 64 feet by 43, provided seating for 612 adults.

FOOTNOTE: Most of the foregoing information has been collected from the editions of the *Dumfries Courier* of 1832. The assistance of the staff of the Reference Department, Dumfries Public Library, is gladly acknowledged. More details can be found in the work of the Dumfries historian, William McDowall—in particular in his *History of Dumfries* (1906) and *Memorials of St Michael's, the Old Parish Churchyard of Dumfries* (1876).

No plush pullman seats these, but plain wooden benches without arm-rests, and so capable of accommodating far more children than grown-ups.

Some youngsters unable to find anywhere to sit simply gathered in the gangways, while a few others sneaked upstairs to the forbidden balcony area, clustering in the front rows to watch the film, eat their oranges and sweeties, and no doubt do all the noisy, mischievous things that children do when left to their own devices.

And they had almost free rein, for apart from the manager, two projection staff and the woman who collected entrance money, only a girl selling chocolate and an attendant were on the premises to supervise a boisterous audience of over 700, some of them only toddlers.

When the first reel finished, it was taken to the rewinding room by the assistant operator who, at 15, was scarcely older than some of the afternoon's patrons.

He rewound the film, placed it in its flat, circular tin container, fixed the lid on, and laid it down in a corner. He could hardly have chosen a worse place to put it.

The container was resting across the terminals of a six-volt electrical accumulator used to power a panatrope, one of the ingenious musical instruments of the day.

The lad was opening a large box to get out another reel when he heard a hissing sound. He checked a radiator in the corridor outside, suspecting a gas leak.

That fear was unfounded, but he turned round to see smoke coming from the container in the corner. It had caused a short circuit across the accumulator terminals.

Old films were made of nitrate stock, a notoriously unstable substance which when ignited in an enclosed space produces enormous amounts of dense, brown, poisonous fumes, including carbon monoxide.

The young operator immediately saw the danger of fire spreading to the other films stored in the room, grabbed the tin, and raced to a side door which opened on to steps leading to waste ground.

If he could have thrown the container out into the open air, the ensuing disaster could have been avoided. But the door would not budge.

Leaving the smouldering canister, he dashed to the projection room to tell Alexander Rosie, the film operator, what had happened. Rosie sent him to inform the manager, and the assistant made for the main hall, ran the length of a side aisle, pushing youngsters out of the way as he went, and found the manager in his first-floor office.

They struggled back through the auditorium. The manager opened the door and kicked the tin outside.

There was no threat now. The poisonous package was out of harm's way. But the damage had already been done, for the smoke had reached the hall, and the children panicked.

Youngsters enjoy the show — minutes later disaster struck.

Seeing that the danger came from the entrance hall, they made for the exits on either side of the stage, then down a short flight of steps to double doors which should have led to safety in the riverside walkway outside.

They managed to force the push bar mechanism on the doors, only to be faced with a final, insurmountable barrier — a locked steel gate.

Meanwhile the last restraining influence inside the cinema was removed as Rosie gave up the unequal struggle of continuing to show the film while smoke poured in through the ventilation system.

Fortunately, help had arrived. With the smoke at last dissapating, firemen, police and volunteers were able to lead the children out through the front doors.

Clearing the hall was a difficult task, carried out in semi-darkness because the control board for turning up the lighting was at the back of the stage, where the first rush of younsters had tried to escape.

Rescuers approaching the building from that end saw bodies pressed against the collapsible metal gate.

When at last they managed to wrench it open, they found a pathetic trail of death and injury leading almost into the hall itself.

In trying to escape a threat which did not exist, the children had created a deadly crush. Seventy died as a result of that panic, and 40 more were badly hurt.

The disaster might not have been so great, indeed might not have happened at all, if it had been possible to open the side door, if there had been more attendants, if over-crowding had not been allowed, or if the metal gate had been open.

However, just as there was no great heroism at the Glen Cinema that day, there was no particular villainy either, to take the blame for the loss of 70 young lives. But of cold, cruel reality, there was a tragic excess.

Death of a Princess

By SHEILA ALLAN

On January 31, 1953, Scotland was shocked by a disaster of enormous proportions. The motor vessel Princess Victoria sank on her journey from Stranraer to Larne with the loss of 133 lives.

This is the story of a happy ship, which came to a sorry end during a spell of stormy weather such as few people had witnessed during their lifetimes. Gales exceeded 100 m.p.h. Much damage occurred on land. Around 300 people lost their lives at sea, and distress calls were sent from 50 ships to wireless stations around the British coast in a space of less than three days.

Early on January 31, the storm had already begun to blow up. The *Clan Macquarrie*, a 7131-ton Glasgow ship, ran aground 10 miles west of the Butt of Lewis in a full WNW gale with gusts of more than 80 m.p.h. Her crew of 40 took to boats.

About 150 families were made homeless, the damage to property occurring mainly in Kincardine, Aberdeen, Banff and Caithness. The fishing industry suffered heavy losses, over 70 boats being damaged during the storm. There was also extensive destruction of woodlands in central and north-east Scotland.

The event which shook the country, however, was the sinking of the *Princess Victoria*. The *Glasgow Herald* editorial on February 3 spoke of a "weekend of disasters with few parallels in recent memory . . . Fortune was wholly unkind"—the *Princess Victoria* had arrived within five miles of Belfast Lough before the decision to abandon ship had to be made. "This has been a disaster unexampled in the history of modern cross-channel steamer sailings," the report went on.

Mr Robert Nish, a dock employee, had been loading cargo aboard the *Victoria* on the morning she sailed for the last time. I spoke to him at his home in Stranraer. "I never saw a storm like that day," he told me. "The ship was tied right at the end of the pier, with her stern facing out to sea. Spray was coming over the stern doors, and the railway wagons at the end of the pier next to the ship were full of sea water."

Later, a meteorologist was to estimate the waves on that day to be 16 feet at 6 a.m., 20 feet at noon, and 26 feet at 3 p.m.

"I saw four Indian pedlars coming down in their car to board the *Princess Victoria*. They were too late though — the gangway was off. Lucky for them," said Mr Nish. "Because of the wind, we couldn't load anything on to the ship. The cranes were blowing about too much. We had to go ashore and resume our normal duties, lifting the gangway and throwing the wire ropes off the bollards. We had to stand by in all weathers until the ship went out, and there was no shelter, unless you could crouch down beside a car. I was soaked to the skin when I got home that day.

"I was talking to Captain Ferguson that morning, and he waved to my workmate and me from the bridge, as he always did as the *Princess Victoria* went out. I was amazed to see her leaving on such a morning."

The *Princess Victoria* had been due to leave Stranraer at 7 a.m., but she delayed until 7.45 a.m. since the boat train from London was late. The crossing normally took around 2½ hours. Launched in 1947, and designed to carry passengers, cargo and vehicles, the 2694-ton ship had three decks for passengers and a spacious car deck at the after end. The stern above the hull was open except for a 5½-foot high steel door which opened back in two parts to allow car access. When closed, the doors were secured with strong bolts — thick stays made of steel.

Captain James Ferguson was a married man with two sons. He had been the master of cross-channel passenger ships for almost 20 years.

David Broadfoot, the radio officer, was on relief duty from his own ship, the *Princess Margaret*. A radio message warned him to expect a rough crossing, as the wind was blowing 75 m.p.h. and increasing.

Shortly after leaving Stranraer, the *Victoria* ran into heavy seas, and trouble developed when she left the shelter of Loch Ryan. Leaving her normal course, she travelled north into the wind, apparently in an attempt to return to Loch Ryan stern first. Five or ten minutes after she had emerged from Loch Ryan, Angus Nelson, R.N., and two others were ordered to release the bow rudder. This proved an impossible task, and as Mr Nelson returned to the bridge to report the matter, he noticed that the ship had developed a slight list to starboard. The cause of the list was the sea breaking over and bursting open the stern doors. The car deck soon became awash.

At 9.46 a.m., John Maxwell, the radio officer at Stranraer Harbour, received a message from the *Princess Victoria:*

"Hove to off the mouth of Loch Ryan. Vessel not under command. Urgent assistance of tug required."

Maxwell immediately phoned Lloyd's agent to ask him to secure a tug or tugs. On phoning Cairnryan port, he learned that there were no tugs available there. In the meantime, the cargo steamer, the *Campbell,* would go out. Lloyd's agent reported back that the Steel and Bennie tugs were sheltering from the weather, and not available. Maxwell suggested trying Belfast.

Meanwhile aboard the *Princess Victoria,* the list to starboard was increasing. Tony McQuiston, a cargo man, described the unsuccessful attempts by crew members to close the doors on the car deck as water poured in. By about 10.30 a.m., when he was last on the car deck, part of the cargo, such as mail bags and parcels, had begun to shift. The water was about 5½ feet deep and reached up to the portholes.

At about 10 a.m., the passengers were told to put on their lifejackets and proceed to upper decks. Tony McQuiston and other members of the crew helped the passengers into their lifejackets, while an officer and some other seamen went to prepare the lifeboats, four on each side of the vessel.

At 10.31 a.m., the first S.O.S. was sent out, and two minutes later, Portpatrick received the message:

"From the *Princess Victoria:* 4 miles N.W. of Corsewall. Car deck flooded. Heavy list to starboard. Require immediate assistance. Ship not under command."

The lifeboat crew at Portpatrick was assembled. John Maxwell in Stranraer Harbour Marine Dept., learned that the *Campbell* was about to leave Cairnryan. From Gourock, he received a message that the destroyer *Contest* had left Rothesay. Lloyd's agent phoned to report that there were no tugs available at Belfast. The tug *Salveda* had been located at Kildonan at 11.30 a.m. and was due to reach the *Princess Victoria* at around 1.30 p.m. The lifeboat *Jeanie Speirs* was also out to the rescue.

By the time the *Contest* had come clear of Arran, she had sustained damage to one of her boats and injury to two men.

James Blair from Larne, a smokeroom attendant, spoke of the calm behaviour of the passengers aboard the *Princess Victoria* at this time. No one could stand, and the passengers were all sliding to starboard. Some tried to get to the boat deck, but most had to hold on where they were. People did not seem to realise that the ship was going down.

At 1 p.m., the first announcement of B.B.C. radio news was that the *Princess Victoria* was in difficulities off the Scottish coast. In fact, she was then probably only 7 miles from Blackhead, the headland at the north shore of Belfast Lough.

The ship's engines stopped at 1.08 p.m. On contacting the *Contest,* David Broadfoot was told that she could not see the *Princess Victoria,* and that the soonest she could be in the area would be 2.15 p.m. With the engines stopped and the vessel on her beam ends, there was ony one option left.

At 1.13 p.m., Portpatrick radio station reported that preparations to abandon ship were under way.

John Maxwell at Stranraer Harbour contacted Cairnryan, and emergency action was adopted. All hotels in Stranraer were ready with food and beds. The local bus company patrolled the area looking for wreckage.

At 1.47 p.m., Portpatrick received the following message from the *Princess Victoria:*

"Captain says he can see . . . lighthouse . . . opeltnd . . . off entrance to Belfast Lough. Sorry for Morse!"

Portpatrick radio replied: "Is it Copeland?"

Princess Victoria: "Yes."

Portpatrick: "Can you get a bearing?"

Princess Victoria: "Sorry. Can't see it for squall."

At 1.54 p.m., *Princess Victoria's* radio officer gave his position as five miles east of Copelands, and then repeated the signal four minutes later. This was the last signal that David Broadfoot made. His efforts were given special mention at the subsequent inquiry.

A blast of the siren gave the signal to abandon ship, after which she could be felt sinking. Pandemonium broke out. People tried to jump over the port side, while others stayed at the port rail and were swept away to sea.

James Blair decided to go the other way from everyone else. He scrambled on to the side of the ship, and found himself sitting on top of the keel. Around him was great panic, and many people in the sea.

"I didn't know what to do next," he said, "I couldn't see how I could help myself any more."

Suddenly, at the very end of the ship, he saw a lifeboat with people in it. Slithering along the keel, he reached the end of the ship, and jumped into the lifeboat. He was only in it seconds when it was bashed against the side of the *Princess Victoria* and everyone was thrown out. He was carried by the tide round the stern of the *Victoria,* managed to avoid her propellers, and, once in the open sea, caught sight of another lifeboat 20 or 30 yards away.

"It took me a while to get to it," said Mr Blair. "One of the chaps pulled me in."

Forty-three men survived the disaster. A total of 133, including all the women and children on board, were lost.

At the time, it was impossible to compile an accurate total of those missing, because passenger lists were not made up for the Stranraer-Larne crossing. Relatives and friends of passengers were asked to inquire about possible victims.

Rescue ships were hampered, not only be the storm, but also by the confusion over the exact position of the *Princess Victoria*. William McConnell, coxswain of the Portpatrick lifeboat, who received the R.N.L.I. bronze medal for his part in the rescue, described how his lifeboat travelled 12 miles on the wrong course, and at half speed because of the hurricane force wind, mountainous seas and nil visibility. In all, she spent 17½ hours at sea searching for *Princess Victoria* survivors. She found only 2 men on a raft. One of them, William Copley, was literally hooked out of the water.

Captain James Kelly, master of the tanker *Pass of Drumochter,* said that he could have saved more lives if he had been given proper directions. After hearing the announcement on B.B.C. news at 1 p.m., he set off at full steam ahead for the Scottish coast. It was the sighting of oil and wreckage that told him he had finally found the *Princess Victoria.*

He sighted a lifeboat with about 30 people in it, put a line aboard and came up close to it. A ladder was thrown over the *Pass of Drumochter's* stern, and passengers on the lifeboat were asked to jump on to the ladder one at a time. The first man to try, John McKnight, missed the ladder and fell into the sea. The tops of four fingers were chopped off, but he managed to hang on to the lifeboat. The *Pass of Drumochter* then had to cut the line, since she was in danger of crushing the lifeboat. The other lifeboat passengers were unaware at first that McKnight was still hanging on, until a loudhailer message from the *Pass of Drumochter* told them that he was there. A seaman managed to haul him aboard, and the lifeboat remained in the shelter of the *Pass of Drumochter* until the Donahadee lifeboat arrived and transferred survivors on board.

Among those lost in the disaster was Captain Ferguson, who was last seen standing at the salute as the ship went down. Sir Walter Smiles, the Member of Parliament for North Down, was also a victim. Normally, he and other Ulster Unionists would have left for home on Thursday evening, and he would probably have done so this time but for the important debate on the Sunday Observance Bill, which took place on Friday, 30th. His intention was to fly from London to Northern Ireland, but when the flight was cancelled, he took the train to Stranraer to join the *Princess Victoria.* Major J. Maynard Sinclair, Northern Ireland Minister of Finance, was another victim of the shipwreck.

The early stories from survivors were heart-rending. Some who did manage to struggle into a lifeboat found that their hands were so cold that they could not undo the painter attaching the boat to the *Princess*

Victoria. Some even tried using their teeth, but to no avail. When the *Princess Victoria* sank, the boat was thrown into the air and came down with a bang, which caused the rope to come free.

A survivor who was on a raft described how two of the other occupants were washed off. The young cabin boy who was also on the raft seemed to have seen something. He stood up, and a strange calm came over him. He began to sing "The Lord's My Shepherd". Then he stepped off the raft into the water.

Even now, 30 years later, it is difficult to find anyone who will talk about the disaster. Captain Ferguson's son, in a later television interview, said, "Every time this tragedy is talked about and brought to the surface, it has an effect . . . It leaves scars that you never get rid of. You have them all your life."

Some people reflected on their lucky escapes. Twenty-four of the 162 factory employees of the Short Bros. and Harland branch aircraft factory at Wig Bay were among those missing, but another 14 escaped tragedy by deciding to travel to the Rangers v. East Fife football match in Glasgow, instead of taking advantage of free travel allowed every two months to their homes in Ulster. Tragically, the "free weekend" had been advanced by two weeks.

Other people cancelled their crossing for different reasons. Mr and Mrs Victor Large, who had five children aged between 1½ and 8½, had intended to travel on the *Princess Victoria* to complete arrangements for their return to Northern Ireland. One of the children, Victor, developed appendicitis on Friday morning, and was taken to Seafield Hospital in Ayr.

Thomas Frame, an employee at Wig Bay and former Irish international footballer, got up at 6 a.m. to catch the *Princess Victoria,* but, being a poor sailor, turned back from the quayside when he saw the weather conditions.

The work of police, post office workers and railwaymen in passing information to relatives continued thoughout the nights of Saturday January 31, and Sunday February 1. Tom Dyer, a postman from Stranraer, finally reached the family of John McKnight, the *Princess Victoria's* cook, at 11 p.m. on Saturday night, at the second attempt after his car had been bogged down in a pool of sea water which had blown on to the coast road. John McKnight, who had returned from honeymoon only two days before the tragedy, was the third brother in his family to survive a shipwreck.

A *Princess Victoria* Disaster Fund began in Belfast on March 23, 1953, and continued until May 1. At 22 days long, it was only 6 days short of the *Titanic* enquiry. Sixty-six witnesses appeared and more than 12 lawyers. The publication of the findings was postponed because of the coronation.

The results of the inquiry, published on June 12, found fault with the owners and managers of the *Princess Victoria* for neglecting to act upon the two previous occasions, in 1949 and 1951, when she had taken water. It should have been realised then that the stern doors were capable of being burst open, and that the scuppers and the drainage pumps were inadequate for clearing the water quickly enough.

After an appeal, the inquiry results were modified, clearing the present management from blame. Fault was still found to lie with those who had failed to act upon the 1951 incident.

It is easy to lay blame with hindsight, but only fair to remember that a tragic combination of circumstances was responsible for the events of January 31, 1953. The weather conditions were as bad as, if not worse than, any experienced by the masters of ships out that day in the area. All other vessels, except the tug *Salveda*, were farther down the channel at the time. The last position given by the *Princess Victoria* seems to have been mistaken: the lighthouse seen was probably Blackhead and not Copelands. It was impossible to launch the lifeboats in the final stages because of the list to starboard. Many of the women and children could not come to the upper decks because of seasickness.

As a result of the findings, action was taken by Mr A. T. Lennox-Boyd, the Minister of Transport, to prevent the recurrence of a similar tragedy.

Today on Stranraer's seafront, a monument of rocks topped with an anchor bears the inscription:

"On the morning of 31st January, 1953, the M. V. *Princess Victoria* left the East Pier, Stranraer, to make the normal crossing to Larne. Off Corsewall Point, the ship encountered the full fury of the gale which that day caused so much damage and loss of life throughout the country, and, despite the valiant efforts of her crew, the lifeboatmen and other seafarers, the *Princess Victoria* foundered off the coast of Northern Ireland with the loss of 133 lives. Of these lost, 23 were inhabitants of Stranraer, whose death this communtiy mourns."

The author would like to to acknowledge the help of the staff and friends of Stranraer Library and Museum, Mr Robert Nish, Mr Sandy Rankin, and all others who provided information.

The mine became
a burning hell

By IAN ANSDELL

Industrial Lanarkshire was a power-house of Victorian Britain. The flag that flew proudly over our late 19th century dominions from Afghanistan to Africa was there not only because of the the exploits of soldiers, merchants and administrators.

Behind them stretched a chain of achievement anchored in the steel mills, factories and mines of the old country, and the price of greatness was paid as heavily at the coal face as on the battlefield. Sometimes that price was high indeed.

In 1877, within a two-mile radius of Hamilton, about 4,000 people worked at 14 collieries encompassing 32 pits. All of the collieries gave off firedamp — pure inflammable gas which issued silently from the dry splint seams.

One such was Blantyre Colliery, which employed about 500 and had yielded some 880,000 tons in five years of operation. There were four working pits, with a fifth shaft for delivering coal to the surface.

Most of the work was done by the 'stoop and room' method whereby corridors twelve feet wide were excavated around pillars of coal 20 yards square. The pillars, comprising 70 per cent of the seam, would be cleared later.

In the meantime, between the working faces and the shafts lay labyrinths comprising several miles of passages spread over more than 140 acres.

These areas were either bricked off or blocked with temporary wooden partitions known as bratticing, in order to channel to the coal face the 50,000 cubic feet of air that was sent into the pit every minute.

The miners found firedamp a constant companion. Excavation at the workings off Number 2 shaft was carried on beneath a covering of gas up to a foot thick at the face, tailing off for ten yards behind.

Occasionally the open oil lamps which the miners wore in their bonnets for illumination kindled the deadly canopy, and the men had to throw themselves to the floor as the flame passed over them.

Generally the ventilation system was equal to the task of removing the worst of the firedamp, but on August, 15, 1877, an accumulation appeared in Number 2 at the 'stoopings', where pillars were being cut away.

Five days later there was an explosion in which two men were burned, one of them fatally.

Gas continued to be found in large quantities during the early weeks of October, and some roof falls hindered the air supply, but Joseph Gilmour, the oversman, was reassuring.

"There is no danger," he said. "There will not be a man fallen in the pit.".

By Friday, October 18, though the air was beginning to turn stagnant and the miners became increasingly worried as explosives were still being used at the stoopings.

Robert Eadie, one of the firemen who supervised the work, stayed away that day and the next, telling his family that there was enough gas to blow the pulleys off the pit-head frame.

Even so, he was among the firemen who went down Number 2 at 4.30 a.m. on Monday 22nd to carry out the routine safety check which preceded every morning shift.

Fifty minutes later they declared the pit satisfactory, and signalled the miners to descend.

At 8.45 the mine became a burning hell.

Only Number 4 shaft, which had reached coal earlier in the year and had no tunnels connecting it with the other shafts, was unaffected.

But on the surface, the explosion blasted flames and steam to the head of Number 3 shaft, flinging men to the ground and badly burning the colliery manager, while smoke and dust erupted from Number 2.

There were no signs at the top of Number 1, but the miners felt the reverberations and immediately came up.

Down below at Numbers 2 and 3, where 233 men and boys had gone to work that morning, there was carnage. By noon, only 27 men had emerged alive.

The cages were still working in Number 2, and seven bodies were found near the foot of the shaft. At Number 3 the cages and ropes had been damaged, with some of the woodwork in the shaft blown out by the force of the explosion.

Descent in a makeshift 'kettle' was blocked by a pile of debris which proved to be 30 feet deep.

Survivors' voices could be heard from the far side. It was decided that the best hope of reaching them was by way of Number 2 pit. Several bodies were found within 20 yards of the shaft foot.

By 10 o'clock at night the rescuers had risked the foul, choking atmosphere to work their way along the communication road. Seventeen corpses were found, and the four people brought up alive died later of their injuries.

Work had to be halted the following day because of the risk of Number 3 shaft collapsing, and shutting off the supply of air underground altogether.

It was Saturday before the search recommenced, and the macabre task of retrieving the dead went on for days afterwards.

Flames had clearly shot through nearly all the working places, and the force of the blast at many points must have been tremendous.

Some bodies were torn apart amid a tangle of props, brickwork, timber and tramways, while others had been overcome by suffocation. Most were burned.

The final death toll was 209, including Gilmour and Eadie, and the

An injured man is given a helping hand.

destruction was such that the cause of the explosion could not be established. But an inquiry revealed practices and circumstances which made it surprising that there had not been a disaster earlier.

Work had been pressed on with too fast to allow the firedamp to disperse properly, and insufficient attention had been paid to reports of the presence of gas.

There was far too much bratticing where there should have been brick walls, and too much of the mine was ventilated by stale air.

Open lights were used instead of the safer Davy lamp. Safety regulations had not been properly adhered to.

It was a catastrophe that need not have happened.

The world has never forgotten Blantyre's most famous son, David Livingstone, who had died four years earlier in Africa.

We are less eager to call to mind his 209 fellow townsfolk, or the other miners who over the years have lost their lives in dark places close to home.

Day the bank collapsed

By KENT MAIR

The crowd in Glasgow's Virginia Street was in a state of panic. Scotland's mightiest city had just been gripped by one of the worst disasters in its long history.

But this was a disaster with a difference.

No lives had been lost. No buildings, trains or ships destroyed.

The calamity was of a very different kind — the City Bank had failed.

Hundreds of people were financially ruined, subsequent police investigations uncovered deception on a massive scale, and prosperous businesses all over Scotland were forced to close.

It was a far cry from the launch of the bank some 40 years earlier in 1839 which was dedicated to throwing aside the stuffy attitudes of other banking houses. The City Bank would reflect the rapid rise of Glasgow as a major trading and commercial centre by adopting dynamic business techniques.

From headquarters at 24 Virginia Street the bank built up a network of 133 branches after its launch with initial capital of £750,000.

A sign, perhaps, of trouble ahead came in 1857 when payments were suspended for a month until the bank's affairs could be sorted out. The directors appeared to ride this particular storm successfully.

Then in September, 1878, came the first clue to the disaster. An item in the Glasgow News by their London correspondent stated that an unnamed Scottish bank was in financial trouble.

As this news was being discussed over the breakfast tables and in the city clubs anxious directors of the bank were meeting in the knowledge that they needed some £500,000 to see the crisis through.

From there events moved swiftly.

September 28: An examination of the books by an accountant reveals a hopeless situation.

October 1: The doors of the bank close for business. The city is in uproar.

October 18: Report by independent auditors discloses that the deficiency to be made up by unhappy shareholders amounts to £5,190,983 11s 3d. Balance sheets had been falsified. More than £7 million of bad debts had been treated as available assets.

November 30: Holders of capital stock issued with a call for £500 per cent on their holdings to be paid by February 24, 1879.

For our Victorian forefathers this was the equivalent of the Wall Street crash. Wealthy citizens were ruined. Businesses failed and thousands were thrown out of work.

Only in Inverness was there cheer for some. A delay in the telegram carrying news of the disaster to the branch there meant that some canny Highlanders managed to withdraw £15,000 before the doors were closed.

Meanwhile police investigations had been made and on October 21 the principal directors of the bank were called in for questioning.

From Edinburgh came John Stewart and Henry Inglis. From Newton Mearns came William Taylor. Robert S. Stronach, the general manager, was at his home at 13 Crown Gardens, Dowanhill. John I. Wright was taken from his home at 10 Queens Terrace, Glasgow. Robert Salmond was found while he was visiting a fellow banker. Lewis Potter was found in distressed condition at his son's villa near Bothwell. A cashier by the name of Leresche was detained in his home at Blythswood Square but he later became a witness for the prosecution.

The following Monday the directors were charged with fraud.

A row broke out after the newspapers revealed that Stewart had been allowed bail of £13,000 with three of the others being offered bail at £5000 each.

On January 16, 1879, they were taken from Duke Street Prison to jail in Edinburgh to await trial.

This started four days later and lasted until Friday, January 31.

All were found guilty. Potter and Stronach received 18 months' imprisonment. Lord Justice Clerk Moncrieff conceded that they had acted for what they considered to be the best interests of the bank and they had not been motivated by greed for personal gain.

The others received eight months for publishing balance sheets known to be false.

The Scotsman in a leading article attacked "the absurdly lenient sentences" but for the men involved the outcome of the case was to prove

Anxious citizens read news of the bank disaster.

a life sentence.

All highly respected and influential, active in church and charity work, leaders in their city's affairs, these men were now deserted by former friends and shunned professionally.

None recovered their former status: for them the ring of the proverb's words was all too coldly true.

The higher the climb, the greater the fall . . .

Valuable cargo from wrecked 'Nessmore'

By SIMON MARTIN

Talk to most folk about shipwrecks in the Hebrides and the name of the *Politician* immediately crops up. Sir Compton Mackenzie based his shipwrecked *Cabinet Minister* in his famous tale *Whisky Galore* on the true-life loss of the *Politician* wrecked between Eriskay and South Uist in the Second World War. But she was only one of many ships that came to grief in the Hebrides in the first 50 years of this century. Although there has always been relatively limited shipping movement in the area, numerous vessels have met disaster around the islands. For example, in one lonely little inlet on Sandray, the second island south of Barra in the Outer Hebridean chain, one finds the 4000-ton *Baron Ardrossan* and the 7000-ton *Empire Homer* virtually sitting on top of one another, while Barra has several wrecks.

The area which claims the most steamship wrecks is around the Inner Hebridean islands, Coll and Tiree. Off Coll the skin-diver would find two 6000-ton ships in the *Nevada* and the *Tapti*. Lost in the 1950's, the *Tapti* has not broken up in the normal shallow shipwreck fashion and gives the eerie impression of a complete ship, even down to still having coils of rope on the decking. Islanders will also point out nearby the graves of such ships as the *Angela*, the *Nydaline*, a Norwegian boat whose shipwrecked crew came ashore to hear that the Germans had just invaded their country, the *General Consul Ellisejeffe* with a cargo of reapers, the collier *St. Brandon*, the trawler *Richard Croft* on which six men died when she was lost in the 1950's and several others.

On Tiree there are three wrecks of which parts still stick out of the sea at low water — the timber ship *Malve* and a puffer lost while salvaging from her, the cargo boat *Ingrid* lost in the early years of the Second World War, and the destroyer *Sturdy,* on which there was a tragic loss of life despite the fact the bows amazingly landed not on the rocks but on the grass. Among the other losses are a ship carrying china, examples of which can still be seen on the isle, and the puffer *Lady Isle*, wrecked just a few yards from the tiny harbour at Scarinish.

Perhaps the most colourful wreck of all occurred in the Gunna Sound, the stretch of water between the two islands. There the 4500-ton *Nessmore* crunched on to the rocks without any warning in the dead of night, with the navigator reckoning they were somwhere off the coast of Ireland. From the heaving deck a small lifeboat was lowered, and in the blanketing darkness the men heard the sound of breaking surf. A few moments later their little boat was tossed in the air, overturned and washed on to the beach. All reached safety except one man left shouting for help on the rocks, not trusting himself to try to move at night.

It was an amazed Hebridean shepherd, checking his beasts at first light, who informed the stranded sailor that he was not on the west coast of Ireland, but on the Isle of Coll.

The *Nessmore,* owned by the Barrow company, William Johnston, had left Montreal for Liverpool with cattle and a general cargo. She was hit by severe gales followed by fog so thick that observation was impossible. Captain Hawkett of Barrow, her master, was looking for lighthouses on the Irish coast when he struck on that night of November 20, 1895. Morning revealed the plight of the 340 feet long ship sitting high among a maze of reefs half a mile from the wild and largely uninhabited Coll coast. The bow and stern holds were perched on a reef and as she had struck at high water it seemed likely the hull would become a total loss. The fore and aft holds had 14 feet of water in them and in addition to the 550 head of now terrified cattle there was a valuable and perishable cargo to be saved before the winter gales smashed the helpless hull to pieces.

The *Nessmore* had narrowly escaped an even worse fate. She must have steamed perilously close to the rocks of Skerryvore, graveyard of many a ship before and since a place where a shipwrecked crew are lucky to escape with their lives. She nosed into Gunna Sound, narrowly missing several underwater reefs. *The Oban Times,* reporting the incident, said that even the local West Highland steamers of the time *Hebridean* and *Dunara Castle* would only venture into the area in daylight and then with the utmost caution.

The prize Canadian cattle remained on the *Nessmore* from the time of the wrecking on Wednesday night until the Saturday morning when the sea was almost calm. The beasts had been tended, fed, calmed and comforted by sixteen Canadian cowboys who had also made the trip, and when the weather improved the cattle were thrown overboard. The majority of the struggling and bellowing animals swam the half mile between the vessel and the Coll shore, a few were said to make the much longer trip to Tiree, while others headed for the open sea and were drowned.

Local Coll tradition has it that the cattle which reached Tiree shore were "assisted" by Tiree boatmen, who put nooses around the necks of the swimming beasts and towed them home across the Sound. This tale could be put down to the rivalry that still exists between the islands, or perhaps to the Gaelic ability to improve a tale in the telling, but it is fact that a few weeks after the wrecking six Tiree men boarded Mr.

MacBrayne's *Hebridean* to explain to Sheriff MacLachlan in Oban their involvement with a bullock "washed off the *Nessmore*".

Not only was the *Nessmore* one of the finest steamships from the North-West of England, but she also carried four thousand tons of general cargo, and as soon as the news of the wrecking reached Liverpool the ship's underwriters sent the wrecking steamer *Ranger* to her assistance, fully kitted out with salvage pumps and appliances. The *Ranger* arrived the day after the cattle had been thrown into the sea, and other vessels, too, raced to the island in an effort to save as much of the valuable cargo as possible. The *Quirang,* belonging to Messrs. MacCallum and Company of Glasgow arrived at Coll to bring some of the cattle to Liverpool; the Liverpool tug *Pathfinder* came for the cargo of apples and cheese, while the *Hyaena,* of the Salvage Association came to move in close to the wreck to make the initial recoveries.

The *Nessmore* was listing to starboard and completely surrounded by rocks except for the narrow channel through which she had steamed from the south. This made the salvage operation extremely difficult, for the *Hyaena* had access to the *Nessmore* from the angle which showed her the side and bottom of the wreck, and made salvage from the holds awkward. From there the *Hyaena* transferred the cargo to the bigger steamers lying off-shore at the 30 fathom mark.

It was dangerous work in a confined space, and 12 days after the *Nessmore* grounded the *Hyaena* joined her on the reef. She had been working by the wreck when, as is so liable to happen in the Hebrides at that time of year, a gale sprang up without warning. The *Hyaena* was unable to work herself free in the confined space. For 24 hours she seemed likely to become wreck No. 2, but after "very great exertions and manoeuvering" by the *Pathfinder* at considerable risk to the third ship, she was pulled off and managed to limp to Tobermory, where she was beached for extensive repairs.

The Lloyd's agent and Captain Richard of the Salvage Association were on Coll by this time, and they reported they were well pleased with the operations. The Canadian cows, however, were beginning to cause problems. Coll folk were used to the more sedate Highland cow, and *The Oban Times* recorded that "these wild animals, fresh from the prairies, were declared by the local J.P. as dangerous to the lieges." Despite the efforts of the cowboys and local labourers employed to help with the salvage, several of the beasts ran free, and instructions had to be given for them to be shot. Others became stuck in the bogs surrounding Caoles and were recaptured.

Further problems arose when officialdom clamped down, pointing out that no certificate had been granted giving permission for the beasts to be landed on the isle and they could be a danger to local herds. The sanitary inspector wired the procurator fiscal for instructions, and subsequently the Board of Agriculture granted authority for the reshipment of cattle from Arinagour village, but ordered that no local cattle that had been within three miles of the shipwrecked beasts were to be moved until further notice.

Divers, meantime, had been inspecting the hull of the *Nessmore*, for it was hoped that the lightened vessel might still be floated from the reefs. Six pumps were constantly at work, but the divers found that the bow and stern had been severely damaged and the sternpost and rudder had been wrenched off. The weather, which had been kind to the salvors in November, blew up early in December, and hope for the ship faded. The Salvage Association decided to pull out, waiting only to recover £400 worth of pumping gear.

Island folk anywhere are never sad to see a wreck, so long as there is no loss of life, for there is a policy of "finders keepers" (not recognised by the authorities) when it comes to wreckage brought in by the tides. Coll was to get its jackpot with the *Nevada* in the Second World War, but on this occasion the fates were not with them, for when the *Nessmore* broke up the westerly winds drove large quantities of unsalved cargo, including cheese, flour, ham, apples and musical instruments, to the north-west coast of Mull, Gometra and the Treshnish Isles. The flour was particularly welcomed in Mull, as the salt water had only penetrated half an inch and the remainder made fine bread.

Interest in the wreck gradually cooled. Talk got round to the MacBrayne local coal boat, the *Pelican*, which broke its moorings at Tobermory early in December and became a total loss at the nearby island of Calve, not far from the site of the famous Tobermory galleon. The Salvage Association handed over salvage rights of the *Nessmore* to a Mr. Gash of Greenock, who worked with two steam lighters. In addition to much of the ship's fittings, he recovered 20 tons of cheese, though by February the following year an Arinagour correspondent was complaining of the "frightful odour" of the cheese lying at the pier. The advertising columns of *The Oban Times* were offering cheese for sale in any quantities!

Today one can take one of Coll's finest walks along the ranging sands of Crossapol beach and across the rugged rocks south-west of it to the beach where all the cattle landed and see no trace whatsoever of all that activity of 1895. Indeed, only a handful of islanders could direct you anywhere near the site. However, in 1972 I was a member of a group of young divers who rediscovered the wreck. I had gone to Tiree with Chris Oldfield, a Cheshire man, and Tony Long, a research technician. We were doing salvage work on the *Ingrid* and the *Lady Isle* on Tiree and the *Nevada* on Coll, which are owned by Chris Oldfield, and wanted to examine the *Nessmore* to see if salvage operations there might be commercially viable.

We were put on the trail of the *Nessmore* by Hughie "Handy" — Hugh Mackinnon of Arinagour, who has fished for lobsters all round the coast. Another informant, Willie Mackintosh of Tiree, was able to give us an accurate fix. As a lad he fished with his grandfather who had witnessed all the salvage attempts.

When we explored the wreck we found it had been extensively salvaged at the end of last century. Lying stripped and scattered among the reefs, only the bare outline is left of the once splendid ship.

Cargo included valuable cattle.

Swimming amongst the wreckage now partially buried in sand, we admired the three great boilers and the explosive-shattered concrete remains of the compound steam engine. Twenty feet below the surface, the remains of the *Nessmore* are a monument to the salvage feats and that race against the storms all those years ago.

Grace Darling — the "Forfarshire" heroine

By A. H. MILLAR

There have been wrecks far more destructive of human life than was the wreck of the "Forfarshire" off the Longstone Light in September, 1838; and there may have been actions even more daring and melodramatic than was the courageous rescue of the survivors by Grace Darling. But it may be safely asserted that no heroic action in the last century took so firm a hold upon the emotions of human nature throughout the world as this fearless deed of the heroic English girl.

The gallant work accomplished in the face of tempest and storm, has "given this action deathless fame." Few years were bestowed upon Grace Darling after this crisis in her life but her name will survive among the great heroines of history.

The "Forfarshire" was built at Dundee, in the yard of Mr. Adamson, then one of the most noted local shipbuilders. She was launched in December, 1835, as the largest steamer constructed in a Dundee yard.

The most recent improvements had been used in her construction. The engines were made by Mr. Peter Borrie, the foremost engineer in the locality.

The dimensions of the "Forfarshire" were: Length of keel, 127 feet; deck, 140 feet; breadth over paddles, 40 feet 6 inches; space between wheels, 22 feet 6 inches; burden, 270 tons; horse-power, 190. The main saloon was 36 feet long, and 24 feet broad, and she was specially fitted up as a passenger steamer, to ply between Dundee and Hull.

On Tuesday, May 3, 1836, the "Forfarshire" made her trial trip, under the command of Captain James Kidd, formerly of the London Shipping Company's steamer Perth. This trip was deemed satisfactory, the speed attained being 12 miles an hour, the motion being very steady. After this proof of the vessel's capability, she was put upon the route designed for her.

It may be mentioned that the fares from Dundee to Hull were then as follows:—Main cabin, 20s. (£1); fore cabin, 10s. (50p); deck, 5s. (25p). Arrangements were made whereby passengers could be taken by

Grace was heroine of the hour.

steamer from Hull to London for 2s. (10p): so that the whole journey from Dundee to London in those early days—and with all the inconveniences—might be accomplished for 7s. (35p).

On May 7, 1836, the "Forfarshire" made her first voyage to Hull, outstripping the "Perth"—then the crack steamer on the route—by four miles, though the "Perth" had an hour's start. This auspicious beginning was well maintained, and the "Forfarshire" became the favourite.

The career of the vessel, however, was destined to be brief. For two years and four months she continued to sail without mishap, and the Company was reckoned to be in a flourishing condition, when disaster struck.

On Saturday, September 1, 1838, the "Forfarshire" sailed from Dundee, and arrived safely at Hull. She left that port on her return voyage at 6.30 p.m. on Wednesday, September 5, but she was fated never to enter the Tay. Before she left Dundee there had been complaints about the condition of the boilers. Some hasty repairs had been made at Hull but the vessel had not gone far when a serious leak was discovered in one of the boilers.

Captain John Humble, who was then in charge, tried to remedy the defect without success. It was soon found impossible for the men to remain in the engine-room, as the boiling water flooded the floor, and speedily extinguished the fires.

The captain was naturally anxious, for there were then 63 people on board: 39 passengers, the captain and his wife, 14 seamen, 4 firemen, 2 coal trimmers, and 2 stewards. A fog had settled down to add to the danger, and as it was found impossible to get up steam, the sails had to be hoisted.

John Kidd, one of the survivors of the wreck, who was a fireman on board the "Forfarshire", long afterwards narrated his experiences:

"On the evening of the second day a gale sprang up, and gradually increased in fury, while the rain came down in bucketfuls. It was a terrible night: I never saw anything like it before or since. So far as I can remember, it was about two o'clock in the morning when 'breakers ahead' were reported. Some of the crew noticed the lighthouse at Farne Islands, and we discovered we were out of our course, being about two miles nearer the inner light, where the Darlings lived, than we should have been.

"About a quarter-of-an-hour after the light was first noticed the steamer struck on the Longstone Rock. The sea then made a clean sweep over her, and it was only at intervals that we could manage to get a breath. I was down at the fires when the accident occurred, and on feeling the shock I attempted to get to the deck, but for a time failed. By good luck I clutched hold of the companion door, and for a considerable time—I don't know how long—I held by it.

"From the screams of the passengers as they left their berths, and the ringing of bells, and the hurried orders, I could fancy that the scene on deck must have been a terrible one; but as I was below I did not see it. My neighbour fireman was also hanging on to the companion door alongside of me; but he lost heart, and said to me that he was to let go. I did all in my power to raise his fallen spirits and encourage him, but all was in vain. He lost his hold, but I caught him by the trousers and kept him up for a while until a huge wave rolled over us, and carried him out of my sight into the bosom of the deep. The timbers of the ship then began to give way, and the sides closed like bellows shutting.

"At this juncture of my sufferings I narrowly escaped losing my life. When the sides of the ship came together my head was almost caught, and I only succeeded in getting off with my life with a broken nose (which still bothers me) and a bruise to my head. I managed to retain my hold of the vessel, although huge seas were breaking over her, but I was in an agony of despair.

"I prayed for daylight, and when it did come we found that there were nine of us alive and clinging to the wreck. The tide had ebbed very much by this time, and, though we were greatly benumbed with cold, and more dead than alive, we ventured to look around us, when we saw many dead bodies lying in different parts of the steamer.

"Before the steamer struck on the rock one of the ship's boats was lowered, and nine passengers and several of the crew left in it. They were picked up by a Montrose sloop bound for Shields. When once we nine shipwrecked persons, amongst whom was a lady named Mrs. Dawson, got on to the rocks, we commenced to gather spars from the wreck, and the carpenter proceeded to make a raft with them.

"We considered it unsafe to stay on the rocks, and our intention in making a raft was that when the tide rose it would float, and we would escape on it. None of us had much clothing, and the weather was very cold. I was clad in nothing but a shirt and a pair of trousers, and our sufferings were intense.

"When deploring our fate, however, we caught sight of a boat coming in the direction of the rock, and this put new life into us. The boat was manned by a man and woman, who turned out to be Grace Darling and her father from the Longstone Lighthouse. The boat was a small English coble, which could not take all of us at once.

"Mr. Darling was very careful with his boat when he reached the rock. He rowed about till he could get a chance to come near with safety, and then he shouted for one of us to jump into the little craft. Mrs. Dawson was very much exhausted by this time, and it was with great difficulty that we could get her into the boat safely; in fact, we had to fling her into it.

"I do not remember how many were taken to Mr. Darling's home in the first passage that was made, but after we had landed there our rescuer—Mr. Darling—the carpenter, and I returned for the others, and we were all landed safely at the lighthouse."

The scene of the wreck was the Harkar's Rock, about half-a-mile from the Longstone Lighthouse on the furthermost of the Farne Islands. The keeper of the light was William Darling, who lived on this sea-beat island with his wife and one of his daughters—Grace Horsley Darling.

In the early morning, after that tempestuous night, Grace Darling was awakened by the cries of the shipwrecked party. She woke her father, and when day broke they could see the wreck on the Harkar's Rock. The sea was still raging, and Darling knew it would be impossible for him alone to manage his little coble through the swelling flood.

It was then that Grace volunteered to venture with him. John M'Queen, another of the survivors, described the rescue:—

"It was about nine o'clock when the lifeboat with Grace Darling came alongside of the rock. They touched the South end first, where the father came out, while Grace went a long way round with the boat to the lee-side, where it was more sheltered. I was the first one she spoke to when she touched the wreck. She said, 'Oh, honey, honey, how many more are there of you?'

"I was almost overcome at seeing that a young girl was our rescuer. I said, 'God bless you, woman; God will reward you.' One-half of those on the wreck were taken ashore in the boat by Grace and her father.

"It was very stormy, and I believe that Grace and her father would have been unable to regain Longstone without the assitance of the others, as the tide was also runnning against them. Mr. Darling and two of the sailors returned to the wreck in half-an-hour or so, and took the remainder of us to the lighthouse. Grace Darling dressed my wounds. We were supplied with everything that we required, including clothes. We remained there from the Friday till the Sunday."

Of the 63 persons on board the "Forfarshire", 18 were saved and 45 were drowned. Shortly before the vessel struck, some of the crew came aft and lowered the port quarter boat, intending to keep near the steamer and take off as many as possible. But those on board this little craft—nine men, including one passenger—had only two oars, and they were carried south by the current. After daybreak they were picked up by a sloop belonging to Montrose, and landed at North Shields.

Among the passengers taken off by Grace Darling were:—John Kidd, fireman, Dundee; Jonathan Tickett, cook, Hull; John M'Queen, coal-trimmer, Dundee; John Tulloch, carpenter, Dundee; James Nicholson, fireman, Dundee; Mrs. Dawson of Hull, bound for Dundee, with her two children, both of whom died from exposure on the night of the wreck.

The heroic act of Grace Darling produced many expressions of admiration in all parts of the world. The Duke and Duchess of Northumberland invited William Darling and his daughter to Alnwick Castle, and gave the heroine a present of fifty guineas from Queen Victoria. Grace also received many medals and honours.

It was a brief life of fame, however. Before three years had passed it was known that consumption had marked Grace Darling for its victim. She was taken first to Bamburgh, her birthplace, then to Wooler, and on to Alnwick, where it was seen that death was a question of time. She returned to Bamburgh, and there, tended by her sister Tomasine, she died (less than a fortnight after her arrival) on October 20, 1842, four years after the wreck of the "Forfarshire". She was only 26 years old. Her mother died in 1848; her father in 1865; and that sister Tomasine, who was her tender nurse, died in 1886.

Trapped under tons of moss
By GEORGE SKINNER

On Monday, August 26, 1901, the miners of Donibristle Colliery were working away cheerfully at their grim daily task of "winning coal." I say cheerfully, because having worked underground myself I know the joking and good-humoured banter that goes on amidst the dangers and discomforts of a coal-mine. Before that fateful Monday ended, the Donibristle area, and all the mining villages in Fife, were to be plunged into grief and the deepest despair.

"What happened?" "What went wrong?" These are the questions that miners have been asking ever since. I will try to answer them, or at least describe the events that led up to this terrible tragedy and the heroic deeds that followed.

The Donibristle Companies had sunk the pit to a depth of 97 fathoms, shallow in comparison with present-day sinkings, but deep enough to reach the valuable Dunfermline Splint seam. The other seams being worked were the Mynheer, the Blowlowan and the Parrot.

The Mynheer was 77 fathoms deep but a geological fault (a hitch as miners term it) had thrown the strata up 20 fathoms. This problem was overcome, the coal was "found" again and worked at the higher level.

Now most coal seams (if not all) are on a slope and the Mynheer was no exception. As work progressed, the officials knew they were coming near the outcrop in a field to the south of Cowdenbeath known as Mossmorran Moor. This area consisted of sand, gravel, moss and mud and was 24 feet deep in places. When the coal-seam reached this point, it was decided to drive a heading right through to the surface to improve the air-flow into the pit and also to shorten the journey the men had to make to the coal-face. A long rod, half an inch in diameter, was forced through to the surface. No sign of water was found and it was thought that the moss was dry enough for it to be safe to proceed with the heading to the surface.

Alexander Smith and David Campbell were the two men appointed to this job, which went smoothly enough until that fateful day in August when disaster struck.

It was 2 p.m. when the moss gave way and rushed in a roaring torrent into the workings. Campbell and Smith must have been instantly engulfed and swept to their death. The other men in the seam, realising what had happened, made their way along the airway and escaped through the day mine. Eight were still missing. Of those eight, two died in the mud — a young lad, William Forsyth, and George Hutchison, whose body was carried 500 yards with the rushing moss. The remaining six were trapped in a side road, alive but with little hope of being rescued.

The gravity and horror of what had occurred was now known on the surface at the main shaft. A four-man search-party, led by Thomas Rattray, went underground to look for the missing men, while officials and men rushed to the spot on the Moor where the heading was to emerge. At first glance there was only slight subsidence, but soon this developed into a hole, then into an ever-widening crater with thousands of tons of moss and water tumbling down into the workings.

Mining experts, including Mr. Robert Birrell (manager), Messrs. Bowman, A. Carlow, G. Carlow, Rowan, Nasmyth, Gemmell and other managers from the surrounding area came to the scene and various plans were being suggested to stop the inrush of moss and thereby gain access to the working. They had little hope of finding anyone alive but miners never give up hope, if there is even the slightest chance of saving a comrade.

Many ideas were put forward by men and officails, but it was Birrell and Bowman who decided the course of action that was to prove successful. Their scheme was to erect an aerial roepway across the top of the hole and attach a wooden crib or cage to the ropes, thus enabling an inspection of the hole to be made, clear of the inrushing moss.

The steel ropes and large quantities of timber were carried across the moor and joiners and workmen got to work sawing timber and stretching ropes across the crevasse. Stakes 20 feet long were driven into the ground about 200 yards apart and the ropes were then clamped at one end. Hundreds of strong and eager hands drew the ropes taut and they were fixed securely.

The wooden cage, now completed, was attached to the ropes and two miners entered it and were pulled across until they were directly above the fearsome hole. They lowered a weighted tape into the darkness. It struck the solid floor of the "heading" which proved the incline was clear of moss, and air was getting into the mine.

Mr. Bowman and Mr. Rowan then went out on the cage after their inspection, and now having a direct, though extremely precarious, approach to the hole, they decided to try to barricade and secure the sides of the cavity.

Pit-sinkers, joiners and workmen went to work without delay. Wooden battens, trees, branches and various other materials were used in this dangerous job, and, on completion, the sludge and water going into the hole was greatly reduced.

Birrell and Bowman were then lowered into the hole and, to their surprise and joy, their calls were answered by the entombed men below. This news brought hope where there had only been despondency and the thousands of spectators who had gathered on the scene gave vent to their pent-up emotions with a tremendous cheer that resounded again and again across the Moor.

The condition of the heading was chaotic. Sides and roof had collapsed, and the dangerous work went on, "barring" and securing where possible. It was some time before it was considered safe to try to bring the men to the surface.

From the hundreds of volunteers, James Dick and John Sheddon were the two miners chosen to make the first attempt. They were lowered twenty-five yards into the chasm with a strong hemp rope and a wooden stretcher. A few minutes of agonising suspense elapsed, then came the signal and the first man was brought out. He was John Farquhar, and he was covered with mud but still able to raise a smile. Many questions were put to him, but he could only reply, "Six of us!" Doctors attended to him, then he was led away to safety.

No time was wasted, and John Jones went down on the rope this time. Soon the second man, John Colville, was up in the sunshine. At fifteen-minute intervals three more of the trapped men, Thomas Bauld, Andrew Love and John Beveridge, had been raised to safety.

The method that James Dick, John Sheddon and John Jones had used in rescuing the five men was to tie two loops of hemp rope to the bottom of the lowering rope. The man being rescued was secured to the top loop, and the rescuer to the lower one. The rope was then raised while two of the rescuers stayed below with the trapped men.

When the fifth man was brought up James Dick was with him. Weak and exhausted by his brave efforts, he became entangled in the framework at the surface. The moss caved in again, tumbling with its original force into the mine. Dick made frantic efforts to free himself and Rowan rushed forward with an axe to cut the rope. Luckily, the shaft stood firm and Dick was pulled to safety.

Everyone had to retreat to a safe distance and stand watching helplessly as the hole filled up over three of their comrades still trapped below — Alex Bauld and his two intended rescuers John Sheddon and John Jones. The moss went down the heading for some distance and John Richardson managed to get down so far before being overcome. His was the last attempt made on Tuesday night.

As darkness fell, the crowds of spectators went wearily home, but a party of workmen stayed at the shaft doing all they could to secure it.

Early on the Wednesday morning, work was again started to repair the damage of the previous night. Hundreds of men laboured all day and as night again fell, Mr. Dick, who was a well-known Cowdenbeath grocer, brought along a powerful arc lamp. Unfortunately, this could not be used as insufficient power was available. Then a windlass was brought from the workshop but it couldn't be secured properly and was discarded.

By Thursday, everything possible had been accomplished. The shaft head was secure, the incline made safe and a long rope (of steel this time) was stretched across the moor. Signals from below proved that the men were still alive, so it was decided to bring them all up together. Four loops of hemp rope were tied to the steel one and Robert Law was the chosen volunteer who made the final descent.

When he reached his comrades they were asleep. Soon, after hugs and handshakes they were secured to the lifeline. The signal was given and countless strong arms pulled the four men to the surface.

Robert Law was a "hero" as indeed they all were. He had one regret, though — he had taken a flask of hot Bovril down with him and it was smashed when he got to the men. "Rabbie" thought this had spoiled the show!

The scenes which followed the rescue defy description. Joy and relief was on every face. The thousands who had gathered cheered and cheered again. But there were also many, many tears. Eight men were still down there in the underground "morass". Four of them were known to be dead — Campbell, Smith, Hutchison and the lad Forsyth. The other four were the search-party who had gone down the main-shaft between 2 p.m. and 3 p.m. on the Monday. Nothing had been heard of them since. During all the activity at the moor, groups of men had gone down the main-shaft, and searched every road and brae which was still free of the moss, but without success.

Miners' determination to save the life of a workmate also applies to the recovery of the bodies of victims. Work was started to clear the moss from the mine, a mammoth task which went on for three months. Twelve thousand tons were brought to the surface and large quantities were stowed away into the old roads.

Hutchison's body was found in the level. Forsyth's body was also found behind a stopping where he had died before aid could reach him. The grim hard work continued. Then, on Saturday, December 14, 1901, the bodies of the search party were found in an old road, hemmed in on all sides by the moss.

They were William Hynd, James McDonald, Andrew Paterson and oversman Thomas Rattray. It can only be assumed, but with near certainty, what had happened.

The four men had gone along the main level until they met the impassable moss, which, at this time, must have appeared to be stationary. They retreated up an old brae and got into the road above where they advanced 126 yards only to find it had caved in. They must have worked for some time trying to clear the blocked road without success. When they came out, they had discovered that the moss had moved out of the level and also up the brae, past the end of their road, trapping them. They didn't give in. The next road above was nine yards away and they desperately hacked through the solid. Any miner will tell you how arduous this must have been and how those men must have fought for their lives.

When this upper road was reached it was also closed at both ends, with fallen debris inside, and the evercreeping moss on the outside. Only then had they resigned themselves to their end.

When found, the bodies of James McDonald and William Hynd were close together, one arm under their heads and embracing with the other. Their companions were lying close by, their feet towards them. Their last hours had been spent writing tragic farewell messages to their loved ones at home in the company's time-book carried by Thomas Rattray.

The remains of David Campbell were found later, but of Alexander Smith I cannot say. Perhaps some reader can give the answer.

Gold watches were donated by the editor of the *Daily Telegraph* and the Relief Committee. These, along with money from Andrew Carnegie were presented to Messrs Dick, Sheddon, Jones, Law and Richardson.

Men wrote farewell notes to their loved ones in a time-book.

Many of the other men were given badges for the valour they had displayed.

A fund was set up for the relief of the widows and children of the victims. Poems and songs were composed and sold at one penny each to help the fund and eventually the total subscriptions received amounted to £2765 13s. 1d.

I am sure there was a lot more to the Donibristle tragedy of which I am unaware. Perpaps it would be best to end here with a poem written about the disaster.

The Donibristle Disaster

Between Donibristle and Cowdenbeath,
  Moss Morran's desolate plain does lie,
And here the poor miners met their death,
  Beneath an autumn's dismal sky.

Down in the mine, 'neath that treacherous ground,
  These miners were digging there,
'Twas a serious blunder now we've found:
  They were putting a shaft to the surface for air.

When they heard a noise like loudest thunder,
  And like the rush of a mighty stream,
For an instant they're struck dumb and wonder,
  Then the awful truth the miners glean.

"The moss has burst into the pit, boys,"
  Someone is heard to cry,
Then rings out another voice,
  "Run, run, or we shall all die."

So, with a rush for a safer place they make,
  But, heaven help them, what can they do?
Swiftly the flowing moss is coming in their wake,
  And soon some are hid from view.

Enveloped in that seething mass,
  George Hutchison they see,
One brave fellow tries, but, alas!
  Fails to set his comrade free.

They look into each other's eyes,
  That word good-bye they said:
The terrible moss began to rise,
  And this poor miner was numbered with the dead.

But a hero was left, he stood to the waist,
  In that dark and dismal flood:
It seemed then, too, that death he must taste,
  And be sent to meet his God.

But he strove and battled with might,
And was brought to the surface alive,
Sure he must have thanked God that night,
When for one he was left to survive.

No man can owe a greater love
Than to give his life for his friends,
So we leave the heroes who died to God above
And thus the sad story ends.

Falling flashes of fire
in the great storm

By A. H. MILLER

A furious gale raged over much of Scotland on the evening of Sunday, December 28, 1879, causing chaos in town and country.

About 7 p.m. the train from Edinburgh to Dundee was due at Tay Bridge Station. Railway officials and those waiting to meet passengers wondered whether the train would venture to cross the Firth of Tay in the teeth of the tremendous hurricane. As time passed it was assumed that a decision had been taken to detrain on the Fife side.

Then a rumour spread that the bridge had been blown down. Several eye-witnesses said they had seen a shower of sparks descend rapidly from the rail-level into the river. The idea soon gained ground that a fearful accident had occurred.

A crowd gathered round the signal-box at Esplanade Station. A railway-man told them that the train had been signalled from the south side of the bridge at nine minutes past seven. Exactly five minutes later it entered the bridge.

But at seventeen minutes past when the signalman looked out from his box for its approach he had seen nothing. He tried to signal to the south but found that the means of communication had been interrupted. There seemed, therefore, every probability that a portion of the bridge had fallen, taking the telegraph wires with it.

There was still the possibility that the engine-driver, seeing a gap in the bridge, had been able to pull up and make his way backward to Wormit. In the absence of communication with the southern shore the only way of establishing the position was for someone to go out on the bridge from the Dundee side. This duty fell upon Mr. James Smith, Stationmaster, and Mr. James Roberts, Locomotive Superintendent.

It was no easy task to go on the bridge amid the furiously raging storm, but the duty was courageously undertaken in spite of the fierce gale.

After great exertion and laceration of the hands, caused by clinging to the rails, these two brave men managed to crawl along the line far enough south to see in the darkness a yawning chasm where the high girders should have been.

First evidence of the disaster was afforded by the clouds of spray from the overflow of the broken piping of the Newport Water Supply, which was laid on the bridge course. For a brief space the moon shone out clearly from the driving clouds and it became evident that some of the high girders had disappeared, though they could not ascertain the extent of the disaster.

Where could the train be? Through the spray Mr. Smith thought he saw a red light in the distance, which might be the lamp of the train. Could it have stopped in time to escape destruction?

The two men returned to the shore where a crowd had gathered. Several persons who had witnessed what seemed to indicate disaster, narrated their experiences.

A typical account came from Mr. George Maxwell who was sitting in the front room of his father's home in Magda Green with some friends. This was immediately opposite the two-string girder at the north end of the bridge. About 7.15 p.m. the party heard a crash which sounded like falling slates or chimney cans.

One of the party, recalling that the Edinburgh train was due, suggested that they should watch its progress on the bridge through a gale that was sweeping so wildly down the estuary.

The lights in the room were then lowered and he directed their gaze along the structure. The first object they noticed was the signal-light standing on the north side of the river, a short distance beyond the curve.

Then the lights of the train could be seen advancing along the curve of the line on the Fife side and on to the bridge. They watched the train progress until it reached, as they thought, the third of the high girders.

At this moment a violent gust of wind coincided with three separate streams of fire descending from the bridge elevation and disappearing into the water below.

Total darkness followed.

At first they thought the fire flashes were embers thrown out by the engine-men; but when the train didn't appear to emerge from the girders they feared some disaster.

A powerful telescope was raised and directed towards the bridge. The four men were appalled to see that a decided gap was visible in the structure.

Leaving the house they went up to some open space on the Perth Road and there, in the moonlight, they could clearly see, through a field glass, that the whole of the central high girders had disappeared, carrying the lattice-work pillars with them. No trace of the train was visible.

Meanwhile back at Craig Pier word arrived that several mail-bags from the train had been washed up on the beach at Broughty Ferry.

It was now clear that disaster had struck. The steamer, Dundee, was sent out to try and locate survivors and one of those on board described the state of the bridge:-

"We were a short distance east of pier 28, and from that pier to the Fife side the entire length was evidently intact. Then pier 29 showed a small portion of the ironwork for supporting the girder.

"From that to pier 41 nothing was visible save the stone portions of the piers, over which the storm-driven water was breaking, marking the stretch where the girders ought to have been, like huge-stepping stones.

"It was a pitiful sight and impossible to banish from the mind the thought of the passengers who had the misfortune to be in the ill-fated train.

"The weird aspect which remains of the bridge presented in the moonlight deepened the impression. To these poor passengers the end must have come with terrible swiftness.

"It would be the work of a moment, a sudden crash, and train and girders would fall to the bottom of the storm-tossed estuary in a common ruin."

An immense crowd had gathered at the Craig Pier to await the return of the "Dundee" from her exploring expedition. It was a crowd made pathetic by the excited eagerness of those who had excpected relatives or friends to arrive by this train, and who were kept in a state of agonised suspense until they could have tidings of the nature and extent of the disaster.

Initial reports put the number of passengers at 200 but this was later found to have been an exaggeration. However long and weary months elapsed before accurate information could be obtained. It was known that two guards, the driver, and the stoker, all resident in Dundee, had met sudden death in this tragic fashion. At least 18 passengers were known to be in the train including a bride and groom returning from honeymoon.

It was only when the breaking up of the railway carriages released the bodies, and these were cast on the shore, that a definite figure could be given as to the number of victims.

Between January 9 and March 12 forty bodies were recovered and at a later date no less than 75 corpses had been identified. As some of the supposed passengers were never reported, nor their remains recovered, it may safely be concluded that no less than 80 persons were involved in this terrible disaster . . .

The train itself had consisted of engine, tender, van, three third-class, one second-class and one first-class composite carriages, making a total length of 224 feet six inches, and an approximate weight of about 115 tons.

The engine had some curious adventures after the disaster. When the wreckage was being cleared away it was found near the north portion of the gap left by the fallen girders. On April 7, 1880, it was brought to the surface, but one of the chains snapped and it sank again to the bed of the river. Two days later it was again raised but the slinging chain parted, and it went down off Tayport Lights. From there it was transferred to the

The train just moments before it plunged from the bridge.

railway, and towed on its own wheels to Cowlairs.

There it was repaired and renovated, returning soon to its former duties. In 1900, records show, it was running between Glasgow and the Devon Valley line.

The idea of a bridge spanning the Tay had first been mooted by Thomas Bouch, an engineer of the Edinburgh, Perth and Dundee Railway Company. Directors of the company were amazed by the boldness of his conception and he was looked on as a dreamer. But in October, 1863, a meeting of public and business figures paved the way, so to speak, for the project and a year later application was made for permission to erect a bridge between Newport and Craig Pier. There was opposition but this was overcome and the first stone was laid on July 22, 1871. On September 25, 1877, the first train crossed.

But the bridge's history was brief and after the disaster it remained a ruin for several years. The new replacement bridge was opened on June 20, 1887.

(Adapted from The Tay Bridge Disaster by former Dundee librarian A. H. Miller and published in his book Haunted Dundee.)

The fans tumble down in a giant mass

By IAN ANSDELL

It was January 2, 1971, and the terraces of Ibrox Stadium were packed with over 80,000 spectators drawn from far and near to watch the greatest club match in world football — the Ne'erday game between Rangers and Celtic.

The sounds of The Sash and A Soldier's Song eddied over the park, laced with familiar insults and partisan encouragement to the players as they struggled on a rock-hard pitch to lay on an entertaining game.

There were few ugly scenes among the supporters. This was an exceptionally orderly Old Firm crowd and with full-time approaching and no goals scored, they began drifting away.

Over the public address system, a metallic voice competed with the hubbub to deliver its warning: "Spectators are requested to exercise care on leaving the stadium."

Many of them filtered towards Stairway 13, which led from the east terracing to a car park full of supporters' buses, and to Copeland Road subway station.

Their numbers were swelled in the 89th minute of play, when a Bobby Lennox shot hit the cross-bar and Jimmy Johnstone headed home the rebound to put Celtic into a one-nil lead, and Rangers fans turned away in disappointment.

But they had reckoned without their team's fighting spirit. The Gers stormed back, and 75 seconds later, in injury time, a free kick led to a goal and levelled the score.

The reaction inside the ground was electrifying. Senior police officers described it as "complete pandemonium" and "football mania at its highest".

Fans on Stairway 13 heard the commotion, but there was no question of turning back to see what had happened. That stream of humanity heading down the steep slope to Cairnlea Drive had developed its own momentum.

Ibrox was no stranger to disaster. At a Scotland-England international in 1902, girders supporting a section of wooden terracing snapped, plunging 25 people to their death and injuring over 500 more.

In more recent times, Stairway 13 had accumulated a grim history of its own. On September 16, 1961, the pressure of the crowd snapped the central wooden barrier.

Two men were trampled and crushed to death, 60 others were injured, and onlookers swore that the toll would have been higher if the wooden paling fences bordering the steps had not also given way, allowing fans to escape by spilling on to the slope at the side.

There was another accident in 1967, and then on January 2, 1969, after 85,000 supporters had watched a Rangers victory over Celtic, the central barrier, now made of tubular steel, again proved inadequate for the job.

Over 40 people needed hospital treatment, though incredibly there were no deaths or serious injuries.

Now, at the same fixture and on the same date two years later, there were fans on Stairway 13 who had tasted fear there in previous incidents and realised that once more things were going terribly wrong.

The Rangers Football Club had taken measures to improve saftey, channelling supporters into seven alleys separated by steel handrails and flanked by a reinforced fence over five feet high.

But the human factor can cancel out even the most rigorous precautions. Onlookers in houses opposite the stairway saw one exuberant fan being carried on another's shoulders. Suddenly he toppled over, and the horror began.

The crowd packed so closely together that downward pressure from behind forced people to collapse over those who had already fallen.

With the side barriers holding firm there was no escape, and within minutes bodies were piled six feet deep amid the bent and broken handrails.

The vast majority of supporters had left the game with no idea that there had been any trouble, but soon in pubs, snooker halls and their homes, they heard the first reports of the disaster.

At Ibrox, a fleet of seventeen ambulances was insufficient to cope with the injured and dying. Police and volunteers laid out corpses on the touch-line at the edge of the pitch. The dressing rooms were turned into temporary first-aid stations. And numbed survivors told reporters what

Fans watch the match — death was just a few steps away.

they had seen.

"I suddenly realised I was standing on something soft, and there must have been a break in the crowd around me because I was able to look down. I realised it was a little boy. He was still alive and I managed to get him to his feet. I pulled him against a wooden fence and told him to edge clear by going along it. That was the last I saw of him."

"I looked up and saw a mass of people tumbling down towards me and jumped to one side. If I had not, I am sure I would have been killed myself."

"I was standing upright being crushed as though in a vice when I blacked out. I came to at the bottom of the stairs and just lay there watching the dead being dragged away."

"People were flailing their arms and screaming hysterically, kicking and pushing and trying to fight their way out."

"I tried to protect a little boy in front of me, but I was swept on top of him."

"We were being pushed forward all the time. Suddenly we saw the crowd in front surging forward. People were falling and we couldn't stop. If you had stopped you were done for."

There were pathetic scenes in the aftermath. A policeman weeping as he tried unsuccessfully to give a boy the kiss of life. Two youngsters clutching autograph books and crying, asking a bystander to help them find their big brother.

The following day, as calls from anxious families in North America, Australia and throughout the U.K. poured into Glasgow, the extent of the tragedy became clear.

Sixty-six people were dead, the majority from traumatic asphyxia, the rest from simple asphyxia — suffocation.

Behind the statistics lay heart-breaking stories. Five lads in their early teens from the same street in the Fife town of Markinch would never return.

One man had had doubts about going to the game because of his boy's birthday. He changed his mind, and died on Stairway 13.

Another father was killed along with his son. They had come from Canada on their first visit home since emigrating seven years before, and the match was to have been one of the highlights of the trip.

The Ibrox disaster shocked the world, and overseas heads of state sent messages of condolence to the Prime Minister.

At home, religious differences were forgotten at a Requiem Mass in St. Andrew's Cathedral and a memorial service in Glasgow Cathedral, and a disaster fund launched by the Lord Provost raised almost £400,000 for relatives of the deceased.

Inevitably, questions were asked about how such a catastrophe could have been allowed to happen.

The jury in a subsequent fatal accident inquiry recommended that expert advice should be taken specifically on reducing the number of people using Stairway 13, and generally on "methods of egress from football grounds".

The Sheriff had already suggested to them that there was not enough evidence on precautions or omissions by Rangers F.C. to justify a finding of fault on their part.

But three years later another Sheriff criticised the club for not taking adequate measures to improve crowd exit arrangements after the earlier accidents, and awarded damages of over £26,000 to the widow of one of the disaster victims.

Eventually Rangers' insurers paid out over half a million pounds in compensation.

All football grounds are licensed now, and Stairway 13 is long gone, demolished as part of a redevelopment programme which had made Ibrox one of the safest and most comfortable grounds in Europe.

Lessons have been learned and acted on, yet there are still football enthusiasts who swore on that January afternoon that they would never go to another match, and have kept their promise.

Allan's amazing polar bear adventures

By ARCHIBALD A. LAWRIE

In 1764 the "Briel" of Amsterdam picked up a Scotsman from the ice of the polar sea and returned him to Aberdeen . . . from where he had sailed in 1757. This is the amazing story of what happened to him during the intervening seven years.

Allan Gordon, son of a farm servant was born three miles upriver from Huntly. At eleven he was made apprentice tailor to a crooked little wretch of a man to whom he had to serve and cow-tow hand and foot. He stood him until he could do so no longer and the final parting took place outside the manse at Auchindoir. The master and his apprentice were working there and the elder kept niggling the younger and stabbing him with his needle in order to hurry the proceedings up. Young Gordon let the cat out of the bag by telling the minister that he was being forced to do poor stitching which the minister refused to accept and the pair were thrown out.

A violent fight ensued on the road home after the master had first put Gordon at ease by saying something pleasing only to strike him a most violent blow causing blood to flow from his right eye. When Allan Gordon recovered his senses he landed the tailor a mighty smack on the head with a two-foot long sycamore lap-board which caused the fight to get even fiercer. Gordon records that he was not used to fighting and that the only fighting he had really seen was done by the animals in the fields so he says he copied that . . . namely by turning his back on the enemy and kicking up with both feet like a horse, or charging head down like a ram.

The fight ended with the tailor lying all his length on the ground and Allan Gordon making straight for Aberdeen where he boarded a Hull coaster and so started a series of journeys all over the world which lasted until 1757.

In that fateful year he boarded the "Anne Forbes" under a drunken English captain called John Hughes and set sail for the seventieth degree between Greenland and Iceland where the ship suddenly found itself in the unenviable position of being between two ice-fields which were converging upon each other at great speed . . . one carried on a surface current and the other on an undercurrent.

Gordon was told to climb the topmast to view the impending situation but as he reached the top he saw the ice sheets were about to strike and refused to obey an order to descend again which was just as well because he was catapulted from the masthead onto the icefloe. The ship, meanwhile, along with the entire crew was sucked down only to be thrown up a short time later on the selfsame floe, hull uppermost.

The problem which now faced Gordon was immense for he was separated from the upturned vessel by some hundreds of yards of broken up ice and freezing cold water with no more in his pocket than a miniature New Testament once given to him by his mother. After floundering his way across the intervening space of smashed ice and salt water, nearly drowning half a dozen times in the attempt, he saw that the hull of the boat was impenetrable and set about trying to smash a hole in it with a stump of broken mast. All these attempts made our friend thirsty but he was horrified to find that all the ice appeared to be frozen salt water. The prospect of dying of thirst on an ice-floe in an ocean was about to drive him mad when he chanced to walk across to an ice hill which he tried unsuccessfully to climb but in the process of slipping got a mouthful of ice which to his utter delight and relief was made of fresh water.

This new-found wealth gave him fresh hope and he looked around until he found a boat-hook which he took to the hulk and forced open a cabin window. Inside he found a tremendous mess of broken ice and property and, wonder of wonders, a broken biscuit barrel, upturned and soaked in salt water but holding biscuit gold. He ate the salty hardtack until he was as thirsty as ever and once again made off to his fresh-water iceberg.

Gordon worked his way around the upturned ship as best he could and coming upon the captain's cabin he looked for the bottles of wine which he knew would be there but alas they were all broken. Nevertheless he did find a cask of something which he describes as "either brandy or rum or a mixture of the two". Whatever it was our friend wasted little time in finding a tube and sucking the alcohol up. Whether it was a trick of the Arctic, his strained mental state or his newness to alcohol we will never know but Gordon was quickly overcome by the contents of the barrel and thinks that he lay sucking off and on for probably several months. He remembers virtually nothing but makes judgement only by the length of his beard, and would probably have died of alcohol poisoning but tor the fact that his tube eventually failed to reach the much lowered liquid level.

Sanity came over him once again but at that point he wished it hadn't for he lay absolutely numb by the barrel and kept hearing strange noises from the neighbouring cabins . . . he thought it was the spirits of his dead comrades come to haunt him. As the days passed he was eventually able to get to his feet and stagger to the window to see what was going on. His "polar demons" were but polar bears on the rampage but that was bad enough. They had found that the ship had carried fish and were set upon getting at it. They had found too, under several feet of snow, the body of his late captain which they made a meal of . . . leaving little but a chewed up hat.

Not realising that polar bears were the deadly dangerous creatures that he was later to find out about he picked up a loud hailer and shouted at the pitch of his voice . . . "Avast brothers!". The amazed creatures stood up as one man and ten feet high listening and looking all around. Some began once again to dig in the snow but others began to amble towards the ship . . . from whence the sound came.

Seeing the predicament that he was now in Allan Gordon started to block up the entrance hole to his cabin with an old fire grate but the only way it would fit was with the chimney pointing inwards towards him. He decided to bind as many knives, forks and sharp instruments to planks as possible and so face the bears with an array of pointed steel. Having done this he retired and sang the first part of psalm 107 because he felt sure that his God had never deserted him. The white mountains gathered round the ship, listened then departed.

The next days . . . those leading up to his 21st birthday . . . were given over to making a fire. Luck was not with him however for no matter how he constructed the fireplace his flue device refused to work with the result that he was repeatedly covered in smoke. This problem went on for several days and was not solved until he removed the fireplace from his quarters altogether and placed it at the end of the keel. It then drew beautifully . . . "there was none better in either Aberdeen or London," he says.

The Arctic winter had begun and eternal night was on its way. Gordon decided to undertake a kind of semi-hibernation so he made a tightly fitting snowball to fit his "front door" . . . "tightly fitting" because ofcourse it melted to exactly the right shape to keep out the winter wind.

His winter retiral was however to be broken for one night he suddenly felt very cold with the little window swinging open. Something too was moving in his cabin. He lay there thinking of the dead captain whose clothing he was wearing whose blankets he was wrapped in, whose wine he had drunk and whose cabin he was using. He made up mental excuses about why he had not attempted to rescue the dead body of the captain from the hungry bears, and was fast getting into a mental state of preparation to meet the captain's ghost.

Something was munching biscuits in the corner . . . the thing then moved into the next room and Gordon shivered for half an hour until the phantom returned to munch some more. Ghost or no ghost it couldn't eat the biscuits and armed with a long sharp knife Gordon approached the intruder. The two collided with each other in the darkness and the knife flashed . . . more to frighten the intruder than to kill it . . . however, kill it did, for when the tinder was blown into flame a dead polar bear lay on the ground amid more blood than Gordon had ever seen. Far from being glad that he had slain his possible murderer he was filled with a great sadness.

With a huge white furry body blocking the little window Allan Gordon retired to think. His mind was in a whirl and when in the darkness he heard the munching start up again he thought he was going mad and rushed into a closet and locked himself in.

The Arctic was playing tricks on his mind, he thought. He knew the back half of the bear was dead for he had touched it and yet the front half kept on chewing his biscuit stock!

He could stand the suspense no longer and plucking up courage ne crept from his closet and tugged and tugged the bear inwards from the window in which it was jammed. It was dead alright . . . its tongue was frozen solid so the mystery remained.

At this point Gordon realised that he had killed a mother bear and that somewhere there must be baby bears waiting to be fed. He realised what he had done and wept very bitterly for a long time . . . asking heaven to forgive him.

There was nothing else to do but skin the unfortunate bear and cut up the flesh into meat cubes. He did just that, washed the cabin thoroughly, laid the new bearskin rug on the floor and then went straight to sleep.

He was awakened by a noise that he describes as a "plaintive grumbling" . . . the very noise that had accompanied the biscuit munching of the previous night. On looking up at the window he saw a pair of little white paws and knowing what this would mean almost wept again.

He helped the bear in through the window, and felt his heart would break as the little thing snuggled into its mother's skin, licking it all over. Tears of joy began to flow down the bear's cheek but soon it was whimpering again as it found that its mother was not getting up. The heartbroken sailor wondered what to do and began offering it biscuits which it gulped down. Then he finally hit upon the solution of getting frozen blubber from the hold, cutting it up with a coal axe and feeding the bits to the starving bear. He decided to call the pet Nancy (after the only girl he had ever loved) and he little knew that he had started a marvellous friendship . . . the like of which the world has never seen.

At first the little bear continually tried to fall asleep for it was the time of year when bears hibernated but Gordon kept waking it up and giving it fish so it eventually missed its hibernation and became a tubby playful bundle. It looked upon our shipwrecked friend as one of its own kind and imitated many of his actions . . . even to walking upright. Gordon says it must have been very funny to see himself and the bear out for a walk for he was wearing the captain's old clothing and the bear linked into his arm and walked so that the two looked like an odd couple out for a stroll. Nancy would try hard to laugh in the same way as the sailor and they had fun together making echoes against an iceberg . . . he putting his hands on either side of his mouth and she her paws.

Winter was ending and the perils of Spring were beginning. The snow that had lain a yard thick on the hulk (protecting it from the elements) was beginning to melt and trickle all over the place. Thinking that at some point he might be forced to give up his quarters Gordon took the first steps to looking for a new abode. He started by cutting a staircase up a nearby ice-hill . . . "as large as Berwick Law," he says. Nancy, of course, had great fun sliding down the iceberg and Gordon got a great deal of fun both from watching Nancy and getting the exhilaration of height. For two months he daily hollowed out his crystal palace and he says that its glass-like beauty had to be marvelled at although it was more pleasant to sleep in the old ship.

One day it happened . . . the great ice sheet began to break up. The pair saw this happening to the northwards at first and soon there was a growling from the ice and their bit, like the rest, broke off and began to drift on the very strong current. Nancy had helped to carry much food and equipment up the ice hill so the stores were up there when the need arose. The iceberg rocked and swayed like a ship at sea and slowly began to move but all the time the old ship remained stuck fast in their portion of ice.

With the sudden appearance of open water Gordon feared that he would lose his beloved Nancy but Nancy loved him too much to part and returned from the water each time bearing him gifts of fish, which were either eaten or stored.

After some time it became evident that the ship was very well stuck in the ice still and at that point was not in danger of breaking away. Our friends therefore decided to reinhabit the hulk. After a short while an amazing thing happened for their particular piece of ice floated off by itself till all that could be seen was the sea and even more strangely bits of flotsam shot past them in a northerly direction as they travelled south. They appeared to be on a strongly moving undercurrent going contrary to the surface current.

After some days of travelling thus they began entering a part of the sea where floating ice was more abundant and it appeared that as they kept travelling South the greater became the volume and thickness of this ice until it became apparent that its continual collision with their iceberg would eventually destroy it, large though it was.

It was decided to make a total evacuation of the ship and the two sadly said goodbye to their old home and carried the last of their belongings up to their ice-house hacked from the solid ice far above the level of the ship.

Allan and the bear walk out.

It was just as well that they did what they did when they did because the melting of the iceberg had caused it to tilt and swing round so that now the end of the iceberg which cradled the ship faced into the oncoming waves of floating ice.

Wave after wave smashed up the prow of their floating ice castle until the snarling ice had chewed its way up to the very ship itself which it began to devour with tearing and smashing that left both Nancy and Allan Gordon horrified and saddened as their old home and refuge flew in all directions before their very gaze.

It was ironical that nature, having smashed up their home and having made them think that they were within inches of total disaster, now decided to pilot them into calmer, ice-free waters. Indeed nature piloted them near to land and a glad sight it was too especially when they saw a woman gathering seafood on the rocks. They hailed her as both boy and bear stood together on the top of their pyramid of ice.

To a woman, who from her girlhood had been taught repeatedly that polar bears mean death, either instantaneous or lingering, the sight of a bear and a boy calling out to her from the top of this incoming iceberg was just too much! She dropped the food that she had been gathering regardless of its value and took to her heels!

She was never seen again and the ice floated further south down the Norwegian coast until a second group of humans was sighted.

This time, thought Allan Gordon, things would be different. This time he would sneak up on these local hunters and give them no chance to run for it.

The iceberg ran aground and seizing the opportunity as well as their prized possessions they clambered ashore and headed for the place where they had spied the hunting party from the lofty ice tower. The party had moved on but the eager two followed their tracks changing the hunters to the hunted . . . hunted not for their skins or their flesh but for their company and friendship.

This friendship was not to be easily obtained for on seeing the sailor and the bear approach two things happened . . . firstly some of the men made a mad dive for the nearest trees while the others fell to their knees after a hurried discussion amongst themselves and began to worship Allan Gordon.

Whatever Allan Gordon had expected out of the meeting it was not this! He had come not for veneration and adoration . . . a little friendship and food would suffice!

It was, once again, Nancy that had caused the bother. No hunter north of the Arctic Circle could ever bring himself to view a bear (other than a dead one) without having a sharp harpoon between himself and the hairy foe. This young man must surely be Jesus for who else had the power to walk and talk with such ferocious creatures.

Eventually truth dawned. Eventually and reluctantly the hunters came to the conclusion that they had not, after all, fallen in with Jesus Christ and his pet and would have to make do with returning to their village with a young stranger and a very well watched bear.

The animal proved to be worth its weight in gold for not only could it drag loads further and faster than the villagers but it could catch fish with a speed that astounded them.

The weeks and months went by and the winter nights were worn away by the telling of folk tales many of which naturally told of bears: not bears which caught fish, pulled loads, or walked upright with man arm in arm but bears which came in great herds and destroyed whole villages and ate whole communities.

Allan Gordon found it difficult to believe that some villagers had seen this type of mass rampage even in their own lifespan. Certainly the stories were both so horrific and forceful that although he outwardly gave them little credence inwardly he wondered just what kind of creature a bear was when it roamed as part of a totally animal herd. Little was he to know that he was to find out some years later.

Spring came to the village and love came to our friend. He married and was as affectionate to his wife as he had been to his previous lady friend Nancy. That was the crux of the trouble. Soon the bear, who had had a genuine and lasting love for her master could stand it no longer. With a series of grunts which must have been our equivalent of, "Either she goes or I go!" the bear went to catch her daily fish and alas did not return.

Allan Gordon was disconsolate. They had been a long time together and had seen much that many a man had not. It was a sad loss and one that our sailor did not get over quickly in spite of the love of his wife and eventually the love of his own children as the years passed and he became a fully fledged and acknowledged villager.

Eventually the day of reckoning came; both for the village as a whole and Allan Gordon as an individual. It can more accurately be described as the night of the bear for as the village fathers had predicted, it was only a matter of time until marauding hoards of savage, white shaggy mountain bears tore their village to bits.

The night in question had arrived and Gordon returned to the village as darkness was falling to find polar bears everywhere. Everywhere too was destruction and screams, blood and tears.

Fatherly determination drove him on through the mellee of bears and mess and people to his own house where he found what he had expected . . . savagery all around and his whole family gone.

He was about to do as any father would have done and follow a trail to see what, if anything, remained of his dear ones amid the snow and the wind but he had hardly gone a few paces when out from behind a demolished hut rushed a paw-whirling white mountain bear. It reared, paused, looked at him for a second and then grabbed him tightly round the waist.

It did not tear his head off. It did not bite an arm off. It set off at a jog trot out of the village . . . not in the direction which most of the other bears were heading but towards the flat rocks where the umiyuaks and kiayaks were tied at the side of the water.

There the bear dropped him. It did not linger long but disappeared with a lumbering jolting action back towards the village leaving Allan Gordon wondering and watching as it vanished amid a flurry of snow.

"So many miracles in so few years" he thought to himself and pushed out a kiayak and headed for the open sea.

It was shortly after that, that the whaler "Briel" returning from a successful trip to its home port of Amsterdam sighted and picked up a very cold Scottish sailor in Northern Norwegian waters.

The master decided to return him to Aberdeen from whence he had come and set course accordingly.

Allan Gordon set foot again on his native soil in 1764 . . . seven years after he had set out on his illfated voyage.

He had the wisdom to search out a schoolmaster and record in detail his marvellous adventures so that they would not be lost to posterity.